LIPPINCOTT

Phonics

Level C

McGraw-Hill
School Division

NEW YORK   FARMINGTON

Program Consultant

Mark E. Jewell, Ph.D.
Reading/Language Arts Coordinator
Highline Public Schools
Burien, Washington

Alphabet Font Used With Permission of Zaner-Bloser.

McGraw-Hill School Division
A Division of The McGraw-Hill Companies

Copyright © 1998 McGraw-Hill School Division, a Division of the Educational and Professional
Publishing Group of The McGraw-Hill Companies, Inc.

McGraw-Hill School Division
1221 Avenue of the Americas
New York, New York 10020

Printed in the United States of America

ISBN 0-02-184378-3 / 2, L. C

1 2 3 4 5 6 7 8 9 POH 02 01 00 99 98 97

ACKNOWLEDGMENTS

Just like in sports, 0:01 is all in the teamwork, and we've had a lot of contributors over the years: Christian Rogers, Mark Giles, Ed McGregor, Kathie Scrobanovich, Gary Belsky, Neil Fine, Brendan O'Connor, Pamela Miller, Tricia Reed, Nancy Weisman, Steve Horne, Lee Berman, Jon Wank, Craig Winston, Roger Jackson, Chris Noble, Kirk Bauer, Kevin Fagan, Tom Murphy, Gabe Kuo, Perry van der Meer, Lynn Crimando, Catriona Ni Aolain, Nik Kleinberg, Siung Tjia, Peter Yates, and the late, great Darrin Perry.

But we've also had three MVPs who took the backpage to both heart and mind, namely John Toolan, Jim Surber, and Henry Lee. We owe a special debt of gratitude to Gary Hoenig and John Papanek, who usually gave us the green light but stopped us when they should have. Deep thanks, as well, to Michael Solomon, who edited the book; Gueorgui Milkov and Anna Katherine Clemmons, who checked it for accuracy; John McCarthy and John Glenn, who saw it through production; and last but not least, Keith Clinkscales, who gave us the opportunity. Have we left anybody out? Wait … thank you, Chad Lowe.   –Steve Wulf

Contents

ir
ur

sir	fir	first	dirt	girl
bird	chirp	third	birth	skirt
fur	purr	burn	burned	turn
turned	turnip	curl	curled	hurt
nurse	turtle	hurled	purse	surprise

ir

Name_____

Write **ir**. Color each picture whose name has the sound of **ir** as in **bird**.

bird

McGraw-Hill School Division

 Helping at Home Your child has been reviewing the *ir* sound. Have him or her design a cool T-shirt on paper. Suggest that he or she illustrate on the T-shirt as many words that have the *ir* sound as possible.

ur

Name_____

Write **ur**. Color each picture whose name has the sound of **ur** as in **turnip**.

turnip

_____

- -

ur

 Helping at Home To practice words with the *ur* sound as in *nurse*, write the following words on paper: *fur, turnip, curb, curl, purse, turtle*. Challenge your child to come up with silly sentences using two or more of these words. Example: *My turtle has a turnip in her purse.*

Introducing /ûr/ *ur*   7

Name_____

Circle the word that names each picture.

1.

skate   (skirt)

2.

purple   puddle

3.

surprise   birds

4.

nurse   nuts

5.

fir   first

6.

purse   purr

7.

turn   third

8.

girl   grill

9.

first   fur

 Helping at Home Your child has been practicing reading and writing words with *ir* and *ur*. This might be a nice time to write an account together of your child's first year. You might write about his or her first words, first steps, first Thanksgiving, and his or her first birthday party.

ar
or

collar	dollar	onward	lizard
forward	backward	caterpillar	cellar
word	work	world	worth
sailor	tailor	doctor	color
favor	flavor	harbor	actor

or

Name_____

Write **or** under each picture whose name has the **or** sound as in **sailor**. Draw lines to match the letters.

sail**or**

1.

_____

o r

2.

_____

3.

_____

4.

_____

or

5.

_____

6.

_____

7.

_____

8.

_____

 Helping at Home To help your child become familiar with words that have the *or* sound as in *worth*, have a sing-down! Choose one of the following words: *sailor, doctor, world, work, color*. How many songs can you think of that contain that word? Example: "I've been *working* on the railroad."

McGraw-Hill School Division

ar

Name _____

Write **ar** under each picture whose name has the same **ar** sound as in **dollar**.
Draw lines to match the letters.

doll**ar**

1.

ar

2.

3.

4.

ar

5.

6.

7.

8.

Helping at Home Your child has been introduced to words that have the *ar* sound as in *sugar*. On a large piece of paper, have your child draw a big sugar bowl and write or draw other *ar* words on it. Examples: *collar, dollar, caterpillar, lizard, blizzard,* and *buzzard.*

Name_____

Circle the word that names each picture.

1.

(sailor)   singer

2.

harbor   dollar

3.

dotted   doctor

4.

color   cover

5.

lizard   liver

6.

collar   work

7.

backward   lizard

8.

world   word

9.

calendar   tailor

 Helping at Home Your child has been learning to read words with *ar* and *or*. To help practice these words, give your child directions such as, "*You may come forward three steps; You may go backward two hops; You may act like a tailor until I count to four.*"

SAILOR MEG

by Anne W. Phillips
illustrated by Jill Banashek

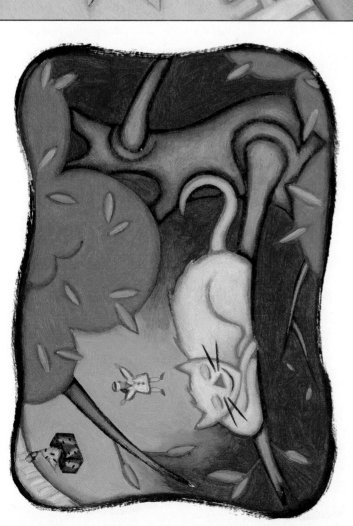

Sailor Meg's boat washed up in the harbor. Sailor Meg checked her boat. "All it needs is a little fixing," she told her First Mate. "Then we can set sail on the next tide."

Sailor Meg fixed the boat. She called to Fur Ball. Where was her First Mate?

At the top of a tall, tall fir tree, Fur Ball just purred.

 Helping at Home Your child has read this book in school. Help him or her read it aloud. Then ask your child to tell you what parts of Meg's trip he or she would enjoy.

8

Meg made a boat in her backyard.
Meg put on her sailor shirt with the big
collar and her sailor hat. She got her
purse and her cat Fur Ball.
"I am Sailor Meg," she told Fur Ball.
"You are my First Mate. My word is law
on this ship."

"Swim!" cried Sailor Meg.
She swam and swam past turtles and
whales and seals.
Back to the snug, quiet harbor she
swam with First Mate Fur Ball.
"Safe at last!" cried Sailor Meg.

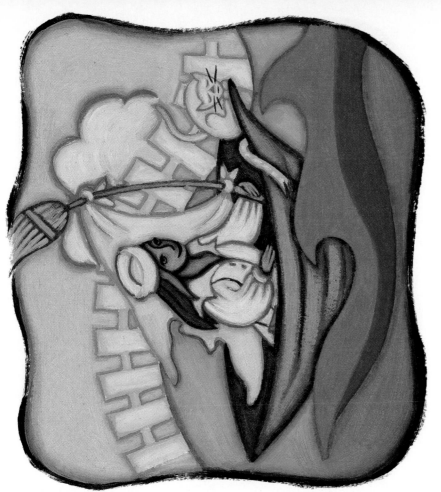

"You have to work hard on a ship," said Sailor Meg. "Pull the rope. Put up the sails. Sail this ship to sea."

But Fur Ball was not a hard worker. So Sailor Meg pulled up the ropes and put up the sails herself. Then she sailed off to see the world with First Mate Fur Ball.

The boat whirled. Waves curled and crashed.

"Get rid of that water!" cried Sailor Meg.

But Fur Ball did not want to get his fur wet.

"The ship is sinking!" yelled Sailor Meg. "Cats and kittens first! Jump, First Mate Fur Ball!"

Sailor Meg sailed forward and backward. She sailed up and down the waves. She sailed past whales and turtles and seals. Onward and forward Sailor Meg sailed.

"Yo, ho, ho!" she cried. "Sailing is fun."

First Mate Fur Ball just stared at the shore.

4

McGraw-Hill School Division

The waves got bigger and bigger in the wide sea. They hurled the boat far and wide.

Sailor Meg cried, "This sea is a grim, green color. A storm must be coming. Turn the ship and sail for home!"

First Mate Fur Ball just curled his tail. So, Sailor Meg turned the ship.

5

ir
ur

Name_____

Choose the word that completes
the sentence. Write the word.

curb	first	surprise	shirt	purse

I.  "What a ___surprise___ !"

2.  He wore a red _____ .

3.  They stop at the _____ .

4.  "I am _____ in line."

5.  "The tickets were in the _____ ."

 Helping at Home To become familiar with words containing *ir* and *ur*, have your child read the advertisements in the local newspaper. Can he or she find words with *ur* or *ir*? Examples: *first, Thursday, purse, shirt, birthday.*

Name_____

Color the pictures whose names have the sound of **or** as in **worth** or **color** or **ar** as in **calendar**.

1.

2.

3.

4.

5.

6.

7.

8.

9.

SUGAR

10.

11.

12.

McGraw-Hill School Division

 Helping at Home To help your child recognize the sounds of *ar* and *or*, have him or her help you make a shopping list and look at labels and signs in the grocery store for words that contain these sounds. Examples: *sugar, colors, collard greens, mustard, flavors, calories.*

Name_____

Circle the missing letters. Then write them.
Read the word.

1.

ir
an

tw__ir__l

2.

or
en

sail____

3.

an
or

act____

4.

ur
or

c____b

5.

ar
re

pol____

6.

ai
ur

b____n

Helping at Home Have your child draw a picture and in it hide pictures whose names have *ir, or, ur,* and *ar.* For example, in a picture of a house, a turtle could be part of a window or hidden in a bush. Then help list the items that friends or family members should hunt for in the drawing.

Name_____

Circle the word that names each picture.

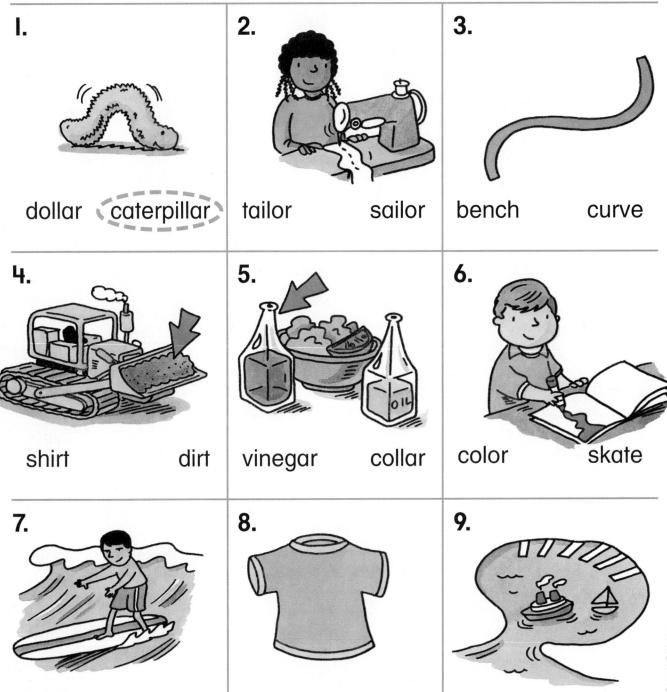

1.

dollar (caterpillar)

2.

tailor   sailor

3.

bench   curve

4.

shirt   dirt

5.

vinegar   collar

6.

color   skate

7.

surf   burn

8.

shawl   shirt

9.

harbor   doctor

 Helping at Home To help your child practice words with *ir, or, ur,* and *ar*, plan a "pretend birthday party" for a friend or a storybook character. Write a make-believe party invitation, using as many of these words as you can: *first, third, world, color, turn, turtle, surprise, birthday, forward, backward.*

ay

Today is your birthday!

Hooray!

day	may	say	way	bay
ray	clay	play	gray	tray
stay	stray	spray	away	relay
today	hurray	someday	birthday	holiday
Saturday	yesterday	maybe	always	swayed

ay

Name _____

Write **ay** under each picture whose name has the same sound as in **clay**.
Draw lines to match the letters.

clay

1.

_____

ay

2.

_____

3.

_____

4.

_____

ay

5.

_____

6.

_____

7.

_____

8.

_____

 Helping at Home To practice words that end like *day*, help your child locate some objects in your home whose names end with this sound. Objects might include spray bottles for water, starch, or perfume; birthday cards; holiday decorations; or objects made of clay.

Yesterday and Today

by Nancy O'Rourke
illustrated by Flora Jew

Yesterday . . .
someone whispered, "It's your birthday!"
You were one year old.

Today . . .
you are much bigger. Who can say what
you will do next? Or who you will be
someday? It's up to you!

 Helping at Home Your child has read this book in school.
Have him or her read it aloud to you. Then ask your child to tell
what he or she could do as a baby and what he or she can do now.

2

Yesterday . . .
a pup sat in the warm rays of the sun. He napped and he played. He played and he napped. That is the way with pups.

McGraw-Hill School Division

Yesterday . . .
little ducklings swam. They went in and out of the water's spray. But they always stayed together.

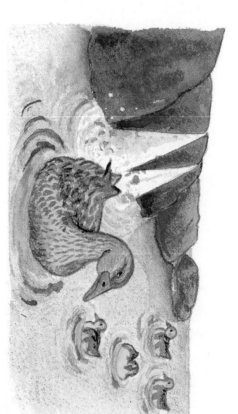

Today . . .
a flock of ducks is going away. They stay together, too. Maybe they will be back someday.

7

Today . . .
a big dog sits in the yard. He can roll over and sit and stay. But he still likes playing best.

Yesterday . . .
small sheep grazed and played. They munched all day on the grass way up in the hills.

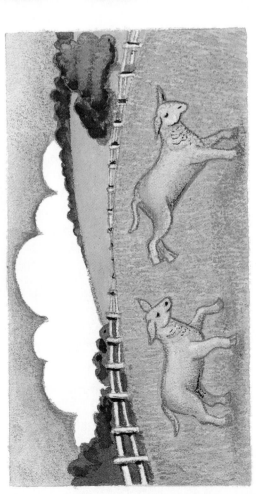

Today . . .
the days are short and cold. Fat white sheep have warm coats. They do not stray far from the barn.

Yesterday . . .
a kitten lay by her mother.
She stayed there all
day, purring.

Today . . .
a gold cat jumps on a tray. She sits by the
clay pots and stares out at the bay.

Yesterday . . .
branches swayed in the wind. Day after
day, a caterpillar held on. It ate and ate.

Today . . .
the branch is bare. Where is the
caterpillar? It got its wings the other
day and fluttered away.

ay

Choose the word that completes the sentence.
Write the word.

| stay | relay | play | pay | tray |

1. We won the _relay_ race.

2. The lunch is on the _____ .

3. We have to _____ for the jeans.

4. The dog has to _____ home.

5. We can _____ in the park.

Helping at Home Your child is learning words that end with the letters *ay*. Play a word association game. Give your child the beginning of some phrases and have him or her respond with words that end like *way*. Phrases include: silver (*tray*), sun's (*rays*), happy (*birthday*), shout (*hurray*).

Practicing /ā/ *ay*   27

Fill in the circle in front of the word that names each picture. Write the word.

1. ○ turn
● burn

b u r n

2. ○ collar
○ ditch

3. ○ third
○ hard

4. ○ tamer
○ tailor

5. ○ hay
○ hat

6. ○ calls
○ curls

7. ○ skirt
○ bird

8. ○ clay
○ clean

9. ○ stay
○ spray

 Helping at Home To practice words with *ay*, play a game. Write these words on cards: *maybe, someday, birthday, play, holiday, yesterday, spray*. Let your child study them for a minute or two. Then ask your child to write the words he or she can remember.

McGraw-Hill School Division

y

by	my	cry	fry	dry
try	sly	fly	sky	why
pry	type	myself	nearby	butterfly

y

Name _____

Write **y**. Color each picture whose name ends like **shy**.

shy

McGraw-Hill School Division

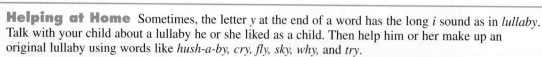

Helping at Home Sometimes, the letter *y* at the end of a word has the long *i* sound as in *lullaby*. Talk with your child about a lullaby he or she liked as a child. Then help him or her make up an original lullaby using words like *hush-a-by, cry, fly, sky, why,* and *try*.

My Friend Sly

by Janet Craig

illustrated by Joy Dunn Keenan

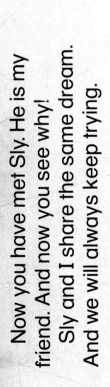

Now you have met Sly. He is my friend. And now you see why! Sly and I share the same dream. And we will always keep trying.

8

Meet Sly. Sly is my friend.
Sly and I share the same dream.
We want to fly up in the sky in a plane some day.
Why?
For the fun of it!

McGraw-Hill School Division

Sly and I got this and that. We put it all together. Then did we fly?
Well, in a way we did. My little plane went up in the sky. And so did Sly's.

Sly saw a bird. He watched it fly.
"Too bad we can't fly," I said.
"We can be birds," said Sly.
"Let's try."
We had fun, but we didn't fly.

We tried to float. But we did not go up.
Not one inch.
"Don't cry," said Sly. "We tried. And we
can keep on trying. I have a plan. Want
to help?"

A butterfly went by. Sly watched it flutter in the sky.

"Too bad we can't fly," I said.

"We can be butterflies," said Sly.

"Let's try."

We flapped and flapped. But we didn't fly.

I blew a bubble into the sky.

We watched it float by.

"That bubble can fly," I said.

"Too bad we can't."

"We can be bubbles," said Sly.

"Let's try. Me first."

y

Name _____

Choose the word that completes the sentence. Write the word.

shy	type	sky	sty	fly

I. The plane can __fly__ fast.

2. My sister is _____ .

3. The pig _____ is clean.

4. The _____ is dark.

5. I like to _____ .

Helping at Home Your child is learning to recognize words in which the final *y* has the sound of long *i* as in *fly*. Give your child an old illustrated magazine and scissors. Have him or her cut out pictures of things that can fly.

Circle the missing letters. Then write them.
Read the word.

1.

(y)
e

t _y_ pe

2.

ay
ea

pl_____

3.

e
y

sk____

4.

oa
ur

n____se

5.

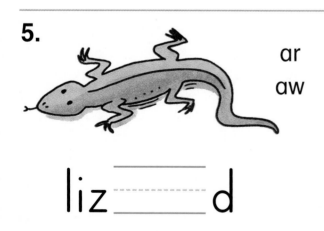

ar
aw

liz____d

6.

ay
ir

st____

Helping at Home Your child can read and write many words in which the final *y* has the long *i* sound. If you have a typewriter or computer, ask your child to type: *by, why, my, fly, try, myself.* If you prefer, give your child crayons or markers and have him use a different color for each letter.

McGraw-Hill School Division

y

any	pretty	easy	dairy	baby
everybody	tiny	lady	lazy	happy
hurry	dirty	many	very	every
party	fifty	hungry	frisky	furry
lucky	Widdy	funny	fairy	story
dizzy	twenty	pony	creepy	body

y

Write **y**. Color each picture whose name ends like **baby**.

baby

y

 Helping at Home Your child is learning to recognize words in which the final *y* has the long *e* sound, as in *baby*. To reinforce this sound, say the following words and ask your child to pantomime each one: *sleepy, funny, frisky, worry, hungry, happy.*

38   Introducing /ē/ *y*

McGraw-Hill School Division

by Ada Evelyn

illustrated by Ethan Long

Miss Widdy's pet was the best of all. It was funny and very smart. Hurray for Miss Widdy!

 Helping at Home Your child has read this book in school. Take turns reading it aloud. Then have your child tell you what he or she likes about Miss Widdy's class.

8

This is my teacher, Miss Widdy.
Miss Widdy's class is a happy class.
I think I am very lucky to have her as
a teacher.

Harry Taylor's pet was just a little bit
creepy. When she saw it, Miss Widdy
didn't look very happy.

In math, Miss Widdy sings funny
songs. One was about the number fifty.
In reading, she reads fairy tales.
We play act every story.

Many of the kids in my class
have pets.
Jenny's pet is a baby fish.
Sandy's pet is very furry.
I am the one with the hamster.

In sports, Miss Widdy comes to every game. She is an amazing lady.

4

But the thing I like best is our Pet Party. Every Friday, someone brings a family pet to class. We read a story about our pets.

MY Pet

5

y

Name _____

Color the pictures whose names have the same ending sound as **strawberry**. Write **y**.

strawberry

1.	**2.**	**3.**	**4.**
	50		
_____	_____	_____	_____
y			

5.	**6.**	**7.**	**8.**
_____	_____	_____	_____

 Helping at Home Your child has been learning words in which the final *y* has the sound of long *e*. Dictate these words: *bunny, kitty, pony, puppy, furry, frisky, hungry, tiny.* Then challenge him or her to write sentences using at least two of the words. Example: *The frisky puppy likes to play.*

Name _____

Circle the word that names each picture.

1. 	**2.** 	**3.** 
(lady) man	sty surfer	actor polar
4. 	**5.** 	**6.** 
dirty fifty	fly fan	turnip bird
7. 	**8.** 	**9.** 
tray try	penny player	peek puppy

 Helping at Home Your child is learning different ending sounds for words. Have your child draw three pictures: a baby, a birthday cake, and a butterfly. Say these words and have your child point to the picture with the same ending sound: *stay, sky, happy, party, play, why, away, worry, city, nearby.*

ly
ey

only	sadly	really	safely	softly
quietly	shortly	sweetly	finally	quickly
swiftly	happily	luckily	carefully	suddenly
key	valley	money	monkey	donkey

ly

Name_____

Read the word. Add **ly** to tell how things happened. Write the new word to complete the sentence.

safe + **ly** → safe**ly**

1.

neat   Ken made his bed very  neatly .

2.

quick   The fox _____ crossed the street.

3.

soft   She spoke very _____ .

4.

brave   The fireman saved the cat _____ .

5.

sudden   It started raining _____ .

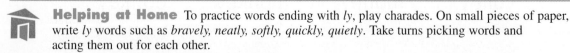

Helping at Home To practice words ending with *ly*, play charades. On small pieces of paper, write *ly* words such as *bravely, neatly, softly, quickly, quietly*. Take turns picking words and acting them out for each other.

McGraw-Hill School Division

Name _____

ey

Write **ey**. Color each picture whose name ends like **valley**.

valley

ey

🏠 **Helping at Home** Your child is learning to recognize words that end with the letters *ey*. To practice this skill, ask your child to answer riddles with words that end with *ey*. Bees make this. (*honey*) Smoke passes through this. (*chimney*) This animal is known for being stubborn. (*donkey*)

Name _____

Circle the word that names each picture.

1.

(neatly)　　　nutty

2.

clay　　　key

3.

honey　　　happy

4.

milky　　　monkey

5.

donkey　　　daily

6.

quilt　　　quietly

SHH

7.

quickly　　　sickly

8.

turkey　　　turnip

9.

really　　　turtle

McGraw-Hill School Division

 Helping at Home Your child is learning words that end in *ly* and *ey*. Have him or her print *ly* and *ey* on two cards. Then say these words: *friendly, honey, donkey, slowly, safely, chimney, quickly, monkey*. Have your child hold up the card that matches the ending sound in each word.

THE MONKEY AND THE LAZY DONKEY

by Eric Coates

illustrated by Kim Wilson Brandt

Donkey looked at Monkey sadly. "Next time," he said slowly, "I think I'll plant the corn myself."

"And the carrots?" asked Monkey.

"And the carrots," said Donkey.

And from that day on, Monkey and Donkey worked together in the green, green valley.

 Helping at Home Your child has read this book in school. Read it aloud. Then you might each draw a face on a finger and use the puppets to act out the story together.

8

In a time far away, Monkey and Donkey lived in a green valley. Monkey worked hard. But not Donkey. He was very, very lazy.

All summer long, Monkey carefully tended the corn.

Donkey lay in the grass, smiling happily. "This time," he said, "I have really tricked him."

When the corn was ripe, Monkey picked the sweet ears of corn at the top of the plant. He gave the bottom of the corn to Donkey.

So one day, Monkey did not do any work. He sat quietly for a long time. Finally he said, "I have a plan!"

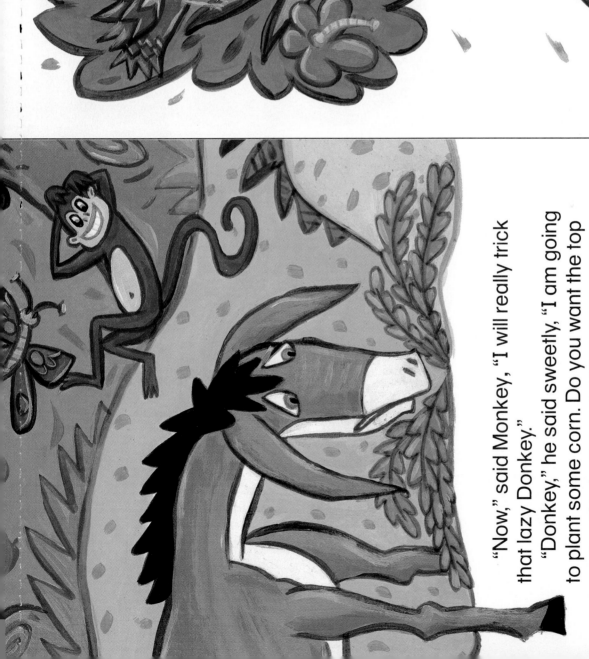

"Now," said Monkey, "I will really trick that lazy Donkey."

"Donkey," he said sweetly, "I am going to plant some corn. Do you want the top part or the bottom part?"

Donkey smiled. He was not going to be tricked this time. "The bottom," he said quickly. "I want the bottom part."

"Donkey," said Monkey sweetly, "I am going to plant some carrots. When I pick them, you can have the top part or you can have the bottom part. Which part do you want?"

"Let me think," said Donkey slowly. Finally he said, "I will take the top part."

Monkey smiled happily and went off to plant the carrots.

Time passed. It was time to pull the carrots.

Monkey ate the bottom parts. They were very tasty.

Donkey was left with the top parts. They really tasted bad.

ly

Choose the word that completes the sentence. Write the word.

| neatly | quietly | quickly | softly | safely |

1.

She plays softly.

2.

The car goes _____ on the track.

3.

He makes his bed _____.

4.

They cross the street _____.

5.

She sings _____.

 Helping at Home To help your child recognize words with the ending *ly*, talk about ways to safely cross a street, ride a bike, and ride in a car. Check to make sure your child correctly demonstrates these procedures when you go out. Use words such as *safely, suddenly, quickly,* and *slowly.*

ey

Name _____

Color the pictures whose names have the same ending sound as **valley**.
Write **ey**.

valley

1. 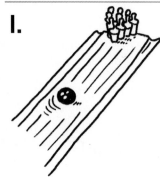 _____ *ey*	**2.** 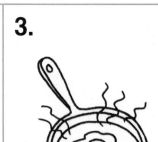 _____ - - - - - - -	**3.**  _____ - - - - - - -	**4.**  _____ - - - - - - -
5.  _____ - - - - - - -	**6.**  _____ - - - - - - -	**7.**  _____ - - - - - - -	**8.**  _____ - - - - - - -

McGraw-Hill School Division

 Helping at Home To practice words that end with *ey*, draw a large key on a piece of paper and illustrate it with *ey* words, such as *turkey, honey, jockey, chimney*. Have your child write the words under the pictures.

54   Practicing /ē/ *ey*

Circle the missing letters. Then write them.
Read the word.

1. ay (ur)

t __ur__ tle

2. ly ey

swift_____

3. ay y

happ____

4. ey or

monk_____

5. y ly

bab____

6. ir y

sh____

 Helping at Home Your child has been learning to read many words that end in *y* with different pronunciations. Look for words ending in *ey, y, ly,* and *ay* the next time you read with your child.

Name_____

Circle the word that names each picture.
Write the word.

1. quickly / quilt

quickly

2. honey / hold

3. key / cry

4. sky / sly

5. fry / fly

6. hungry / hurry

7. play / away

8. bravely / family

9. fifty / finally

McGraw-Hill School Division

soft c

cent	center	cell	celery	cereal
celebrate	ice	mice	nice	face
race	place	space	dance	fence
once	twice	spice	office	sentence
circus	circle	pencil	excited	decide
recipe	medicine			
fancy	lacy	spicy		

ce

Name_____

Circle the pictures whose names have the same ending sound as **fence**. Write **ce**.

fence

1. _____
   ce _____

2. _____
   _____

3. _____
   _____

4. _____
   _____

5. _____
   _____

6. _____
   _____

7. _____
   _____

8. _____
   _____

9. _____
   _____

 Helping at Home When the letter *c* is followed by the letter *e*, the *c* sounds like *s*, as in *face*. To help your child practice recognizing such words, say these words and have your child make a face each time he or she hears a word where *c* sounds like *s*: *place, center, face, twice, act, cement, cast.*

Name_____

Name each picture. Circle **ci** if the name has soft **c** as in **city**. Circle **cy** if the name has soft **c** as in **fancy**.

city    fancy

1.

(ci)   cy

2.

ci   cy

3.

ci   cy

4.

ci   cy

5.

ci   cy

6.

ci   cy

 Helping at Home To help your child practice the soft *c* sound in *city* and *fancy*, help him or her to draw a city and include things whose names contain soft *c* sounds. Possible items: store selling *pencils*; *cement* mixer, store with *ice*, *spicy* peppers, *celery*; *fancy* clothes.

ce
ci
cy

Name_____

Circle the word that completes
the sentence. Write the word.

1. The cook made __spicy__ beans.

spicy
spice
spins

2. The _____ is big.

icy
city
catch

3. The _____ is crunchy.

cereal
celery
color

4. The glove is _____ .

lazy
lime
lacy

5. The mixer makes _____ .

case
cell
cement

 Helping at Home Your child is learning words in which the letter *c* has the sound of *s*. Look through old magazines to make a collage of words or pictures with the soft *c* sound. Possible pictures: spices, lacy, city, cellar, medicine.

The Dream Place

by Walter W. Tilden

illustrated by Phillip Dvorak

Now it is morning.
A circle of sun warms the bed. The cat
licks my face. I look at my wall.
What a nice dream place that was!

Helping at Home Your child has read this book in school. Help him or her to read it aloud to you. Then have your child tell you about the dream place in the story.

It is late. All is quiet. The cat is in the cellar. The dog is sleeping in the center of my rug. I cannot sleep.

McGraw-Hill School Division

Three pigs come over. They are dressed as circus clowns. They dance and do tricks. We munch on celery sticks as we watch.

It is all so exciting! But I am still sleepy. I decide to go back home.

2

7

Wait. Is that my cat on the wall?
I blink once. I blink twice. It does
look like my cat.
   She licks her paw and washes
her face.

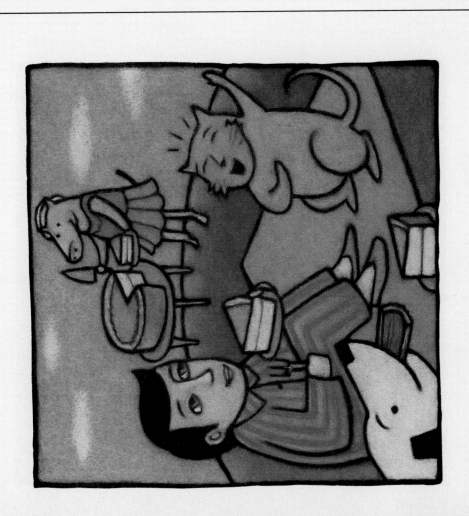

   We sit on the grass. I get a slice of
spice cake from a cow in a fancy dress.
She is celebrating her birthday. I ask the
cow for her cake recipe.
   My cat sings "Happy Birthday"
very nicely.

4

My cat paces back and forth.
She steps into a big circle. She is inside
the wall!
    She stares at me. She wants me to
come, too.
    Why not? I cannot sleep.
I decide to go.

McGraw-Hill School Division

I step into the circle.
I am inside my wall!
    This is like no other place.
Birds chirp in the dark. Bugs with lacy
wings sparkle and float. Nice smells drift
in the air.

5

ce
ci
cy

Name _____

Circle the word that names each picture.
Write the word.

1. cereal
(celery)

celery

2. pencil
pants

3. fancy
fact

4. slide
slice

5. city
silly

6. spicy
spider

7. lucky
lacy

8. icicles
icing

9. circus
mice

Helping at Home To help your child learn words in which the lettter *c* has the sound of *s*, have him or her look for food in the store next time you go shopping. Possible words: *cereal, fancy rice, celery, recipes, lettuce, lacy cookies, spicy peppers.*

ce
ci
cy

Name _____

Choose the word that completes
the sentence. Write the word.

| spicy | rice | pencil | fancy | race |

1.

She has a _fancy_ dress.

2.

They ran a fast _____ .

3.

The peppers are _____ .

4.

The _____ was in the bag.

5.

The _____ is sharp.

McGraw-Hill School Division

Name_____

Circle the word that names each picture.

1.

(fancy)   first

2.

cement   carton

3.

brush   pencil

4.

cereal   circus

5.

clay   tray

6.

color   collar

7.

skirt   spicy

8.

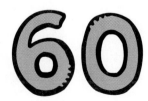

sixty   neatly

9.

face   race

 Helping at Home Write some words on strips of paper: *cereal, valley, cellar, cement, ice, mice, yesterday, space, family, fence, sky, pencil, medicine, fancy, safely, spicy*. Play "Password." Take turns choosing a word and providing a one-word clue for the other person to guess the word.

Name_____

Fill in the circle in front of the missing letters.
Then write them. Read the word.

1.

○ ci ●
○ to

re __ci__ pe

2.

○ or
○ y

dirt____

3.

○ cy
○ ke

la____

4.

○ de
○ ce

sli____

5.

○ te
○ ce

____nt

6.

○ ey
○ ar

chimn____

McGraw-Hill School Division

Helping at Home To practice new words, print the following words on cards and shuffle them: *race, fence, monkey, circle, decide, furry, party, sly, spicy, officer, circus, myself, pencil, excited, holiday, maybe.* Have your child choose a card, say the word, and use it in a sentence.

soft g

germ	gentle	gentleman	general	giant
gigantic	giraffe	gingersnap	age	cage
page	stage	teenager	large	charge
change	strange	stranger	manage	fringe
tragic	damage	bandage	stingy	Gerald

g

Name _____

Circle the pictures whose names begin with the soft **g** sound as in **giant**. Write **g**.

giant

1. _____

2. _____

3. _____

4. _____

5. _____

6. _____

7. _____

8. _____

9. _____

McGraw-Hill School Division

 Helping at Home Your child is learning that words like *giant* begin with soft *g*. Give your child practice by helping her or him say words beginning with soft *g* in sentences. Possible words: *gym, germ, giant, generous, gem, gentle, gigantic, gentleman, genuine, geography, Georgia, geranium.*

Introducing /j/ *g*

g

Name_____

Write **ge**. Color each picture whose name ends with the soft **g** sound as in **stage**.

stage

g e

 Helping at Home Your child is learning to read words ending in *ge*. Give your child practice by pointing out such words the next time you are reading together. Words you might see: *cage, age, charge, manage, stage, page, large, fringe, bandage, strange, damage.*

g

Name_____

Circle the word that names each picture.

1. danger (circled)   range

2. reach   ranger

3. hinge   hunting

4. garden   garbage

5. age   stage

6. giraffe   germs

7. games   gems

8. cage   rage

9. gerbil   garage

Helping at Home To help your child learn the soft *g* sound, draw a large cage and a bag. Cut out or write words with hard and soft *g*'s. Have your child sort them so the soft *g* words go in the cage and those with hard *g* go in the bag.

McGraw-Hill School Division

The Giraffe

by
Cass Hollander

illustrated by
Francesc Rovira

"Yes!" said the teenagers. "Apples are
a nice change. Thanks."
The giraffe wished that he had space
for just one more snack.

 **Helping at Home** Your child has read this book in
school. Take turns reading every other page. Then have him
or her write the words that have the soft g sound, as in *giraffe*.

8

2

Gerald sat on a bench in the park.
He had a bag of gingersnaps.
He ate one and smiled. But something strange happened to the rest of the gingersnaps!

"Someone ate our peanuts!" said the teenagers.
"Well, I did not eat them," said the little girl. "But I have some apples. Do you want to share them with me?"

7

"Someone ate my gingersnaps!" said Gerald.

The gentleman on the bench stared at him.

"Well, I did not not eat them," said the gentleman.

The gentleman went home, thinking about his popcorn.

The teenagers opened their gigantic bag of peanuts. They started to eat some. But something strange happened.

Gerald went home with his mom. The gentleman ate some popcorn and smiled. But something strange happened to his big box of popcorn!

McGraw-Hill School Division

"Someone ate my popcorn!" said the gentleman.

The teenagers on the bench stared at the man.

"Well, we did not eat it," said the teenagers.

g

Name _____

Name the first picture in each row.
Circle the pictures whose names have
the same soft **g** sound. Write **g**.

1.

2.

3.

4.

5.

 Helping at Home Give your child practice with words containing soft *g* by writing these words on
cards: *stranger, mug, manager, elephant, teenager, stingy, fence, glass, gingersnap.* Have your child read
each word and give "thumbs up" if it has soft *g* (the *j* sound) and "thumbs down" if it does not.

g

Name_____

Choose the word that completes the sentence. Write the word.

| gems | cage | fringe | ranger | gentle |

1.  The bunny is ___gentle___ .

2.  Her vest has _____ .

3.  The park _____ helped them.

4.  The _____ are shiny.

5.  The bird is in a _____ .

 Helping at Home To practice reading words ending in *ge*, print the following letters on cards: *gara, hin, ca, lar, frin, banda, pa, char, mana, sta, chan*. Print *ge* on another card. Have your child combine the *ge* card with each of the other cards and read the word he or she has made.

McGraw-Hill School Division

Circle the word that names each picture.

1.

(cage)   stage

2.

clay   stay

3.

stems   gems

4.

mice   mile

5.

harbor   honey

6.

chimney   chime

7.

caller   cellar

8.

flower   fly

9.

cement   celery

Helping at Home To help your child practice reading words with soft *g*, soft *c*, and the *y*, *ay*, and *ey* endings, encourage her or him to point out such words in books, comic strips, menus, street signs, and advertisements.

Name_____

Circle the word that names each picture.
Write the word.

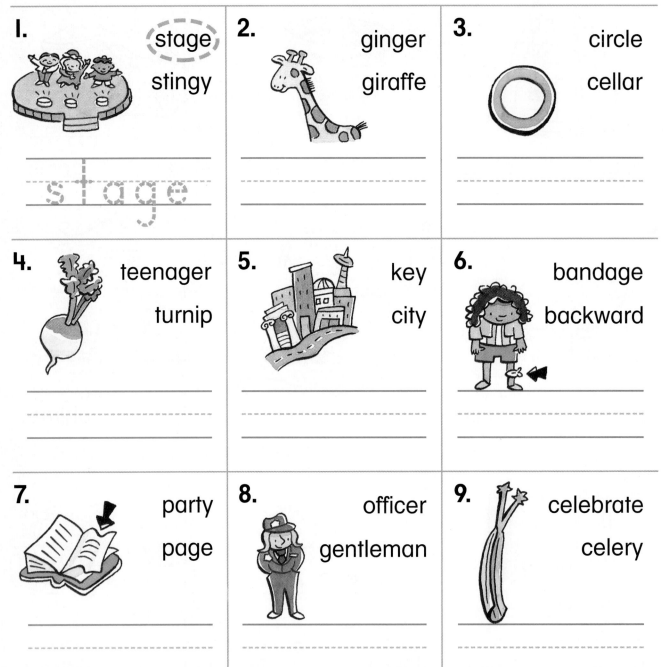

1. stage
       stingy

stage

2. ginger
       giraffe

3. circle
       cellar

4. teenager
       turnip

5. key
       city

6. bandage
       backward

7. party
       page

8. officer
       gentleman

9. celebrate
       celery

Helping at Home For practice have your child write or illustrate words with these sounds: *ir,
or, ur, ar, ay, y, ly, ey,* soft *c,* and soft *g.* Examples: *girl, sailor, turtle, caterpillar, birthday, skydive, baby,
softly, monkey, cereal.*

McGraw-Hill School Division

dge

edge	ledge	hedge	pledge	ridge
bridge	Midge	badge	judge	lodge
smudge	grudge	budge	budget	dodge

dge

Name_____

Write **dge** under each picture whose name has the same ending sound as **edge**. Draw lines to match the letters.

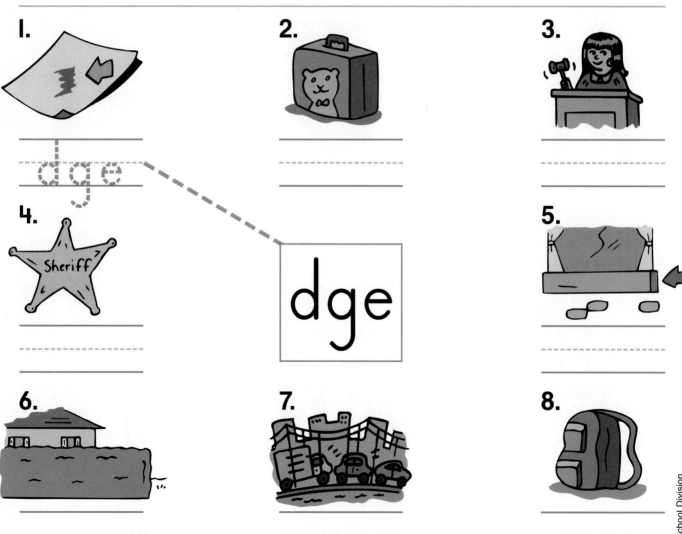

 Helping at Home Your child is learning words that end in *dge*. Give your child practice in recognizing this sound by encouraging her or him to think of words that rhyme with *edge* (*ledge, hedge, pledge*), *ridge* (*bridge*), *judge* (*nudge, smudge, grudge, fudge, budge*), and *dodge* (*lodge*).

FIRE
at Pine Ridge

by Kana Riley
illustrated by Franklin Ayers

At her spot on the ledge, Margo rubbed the rain from her badge. She had done her job. She had helped to save the lodge.

But the next day and all summer long, Margo had to keep watching. She planned to keep her pledge.

 Helping at Home Your child has read this book in school. Have him or her read it aloud to you. Then have your child tell what a fire spotter does.

8

Up on a rocky ledge, Margo scanned the sky. It was a dry summer. Grass was brown. The lodgepole pine trees were dry.

Margo was a fire spotter. When she got her badge, she pledged to watch for fires.

So all day Margo did not budge. She had an important job to do.

McGraw-Hill School Division

The sun went down. Kate felt drops.

"Rain!" she cried.

She ran up and nudged Mack.

"Rain!" she yelled.

A smile lit her smudged face. Mack smiled, too. Now they had rain to help them put out the fire.

One day, Margo saw a smudge in the sky. Smoke! It was in the trees on Pine Ridge!

Quickly she made a call. "Fire!" she yelled. "Over on the ridge! It's hard to judge from here, but it may be near Medicine Circle Lodge."

Mack and his team raced up to the fire with water hoses. Mack dodged a burning branch.

The fire edged closer to the lodge. Mack and his team did not stop. All day they sprayed water on the fire.

Down in the valley, Jack got the call. He ran to a helicopter. Up he went, over the trees.

Now he saw the smudge too—thick, black smoke over Pine Ridge. He checked the bridge. No fire there.

Up in the sky, Jack called out the fire trucks. "The bridge is safe," he said. "But hurry! That fire is getting close to Medicine Circle Lodge."

Fire trucks raced up the ridge. Over the bridge and up the road they went. Kate got out at the lodge.

She called orders to her team: "Cut away all the stuff that will burn. Cut the hedge! Clear the branches!"

dge

Choose the word that completes
the sentence. Write the word.

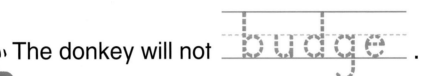

| bridge | budge | ledge | smudge | dodge |

1.

The donkey will not __budge__ .

2.

We like to play _____ ball.

3.

There is a traffic jam on the _____ .

4.

The bird is on the _____ .

5.

There is an ink _____ on her shirt.

 Helping at Home Your child is learning to read and write words that end with *dge*. As you and
your child read together at home, encourage her or him to point out words that end with *dge*. Then help
your child to write the words on a card.

Name _____

Circle the missing letters. Then write them.
Read the word.

1.

(dge)

er

lo **dge** _____

2.

ly

ey

hock _____

3.

ge

ly

garba _____

4.

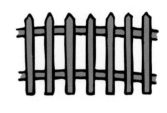

ge

ce

fen _____

5.

ly

dge

ju _____

6.

y

ay

cherr _____

Helping at Home For practice with words that end in *dge*, make two sets of word cards with *bridge, hedge, judge, fudge, badge, smudge, dodge,* and *grudge*. You and your child should each hold one set. Take turns drawing a card from each other's hand and making up a sentence with that word.

sion
tion

vision	mansion	decision	admission
expression	permission	occasion	television
action	nation	station	question
addition	motion	direction	condition
vacation	education	solution	decoration
invitation	celebration	definition	attention
description	invention	position	interruption

sion

Name_____

Write **sion** under each picture whose name has the same ending sound as **vision**. Draw lines to match the letters.

vision

1.

sion

2.

3.

4.

sion

5.

6.

7.

8.

 Helping at Home To give your child practice reading words that end with *sion*, point to words at random as you read together. Ask your child to give "thumbs up" if a word ends with *sion* and "thumbs down" if it does not.

McGraw-Hill School Division

tion

Circle the pictures whose names have the same ending sound as **celebration**.
Write **tion**.

celebration

1.

tion

2.

_____

3.

_____

4.

_____

5.

_____

6.

_____

7.

_____

8. 9-6=3

_____

9.

_____

 Helping at Home Play a riddle game. Say, for example, "I am thinking of a word ending with *tion*. It names a place where you wait for a train." *(station)*. Possible words: *definition, commotion, action, lotion, vacation, addition, attention, promotion, nation, education, invitation, decoration.*

sion
tion

Circle the word that names each picture.

1.

(mansion)   nation

2.

motion decoration

3.

2 - 1 = 1

action subtraction

4.

mission television

5.

admission   lotion

6.

station   decision

7.

3 + 1 = 4

addition mansion

8.

vision   direction

9.

invitation vacation

 Helping at Home   Take turns completing sentences with words containing *sion* and *tion*. For example, "Jan sent Juan an _____ to the party." *(invitation)* Possible words: *explanation, description, decoration, permission, nation, addition, decision, definition.*

McGraw-Hill School Division

THE AMAZING LOTION SOLUTION

by Eric Coates
illustrated by Jan Pyk

"Now I'd like to find another solution for you," said Snuffles.

"What is that?" asked Doctor Giraffe.

"How to make better lotion," said Snuffles. "Let's try pink and purple dots."

"Amazing!" said Doctor G. "Let's go!"

 Helping at Home Your child has read this book in school. Help him or her read it aloud to you. Then together, make a list of amazing lotions and tell what they would do.

8

Snuffles had a case. He went over to Doctor Giraffe's mansion.

"I have an invention—an amazing lotion," Doctor Giraffe said. "It makes people look good. But it is missing. So I made the decision to call you. Can you find it?"

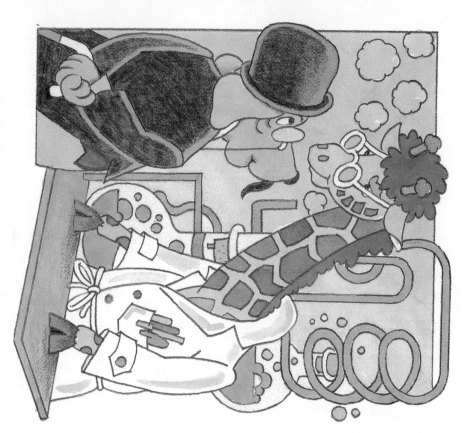

McGraw-Hill School Division

Back at the mansion, Doctor Giraffe was waiting. He asked, "Have you sniffed out an explanation?"

"Yes," said Snuffles. "Three plus two plus five is ten. You gave all ten cans to your friends. You need to pay more attention to your addition!"

"Who knows about the lotion?" asked Snuffles.

"Just my three friends out there."

Doctor Giraffe nodded in the direction of the beach.

"How much of the lotion is missing?" asked Snuffles.

"All of it—ten cans," he said.

Doctor Giraffe's third friend was watching television.

"Pardon my interruption," said Snuffles, "but how many cans of lotion do you have?"

"Five," she bubbled.

Snuffles had a solution.

The doctor's first friend was in an odd condition.

"May I ask you a question?" Snuffles asked. "How many cans of lotion do you have?"

"Doctor Giraffe gave me three cans for my braids," she said.

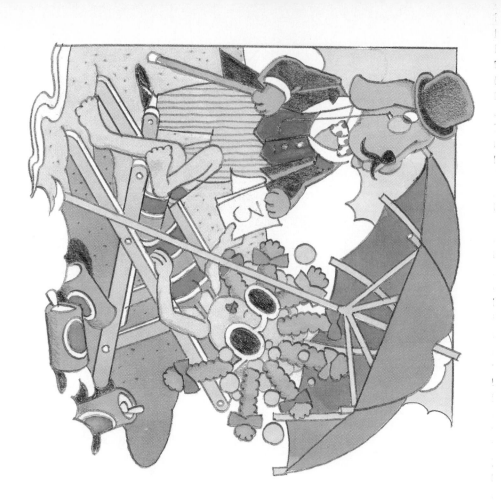

Doctor Giraffe's second friend was in an odd position.

"May I ask you a question?" Snuffles asked. "How many cans of lotion do you have?"

"Doctor Giraffe gave me one for each leg for decoration," he said.

sion
tion

Name _____

Choose the word that completes the sentence.
Write the word.

| lotion vision station decision attention |

1.
We must pay ___attention___ to Mom.

2.
Lily had her _____ tested.

3.
She cannot make a _____ .

4.
Mark put on suntan _____ .

5.
We went to the train _____ .

Helping at Home Your child is learning to read words that end in *sion* and *tion*. Give your child some colored paper and markers to draw a big television set. Write words on a card, including some that end in *sion* and *tion*. Ask your child to write words that end in *sion* and *tion* inside the T.V.

Fill in the circle in front of the missing letters.
Then write them. Read the word.

1.  ● tion

○ dge

sta <u>tion</u>

2.  ○ dge

○ g

fu ____

3.  ○ c

○ g

____iraffe

4.  ○ ge

○ sion

televi____

5.  ○ tion

○ ly

invita____

6.  ○ tion

○ ge

sta____

Helping at Home To give your child added practice with the many new words he or she has learned, encourage him or her to point out words in books, magazines, menus, signs, and other reading materials, and try to read them aloud.

short oo

book	look	took	nook	hook
cook	brook	shook	wood	good
hood	stood	wool	foot	football
wooden	bookstore	cookbook	understood	good-bye

OO

Name _____

Write **oo**. Color each picture whose name has the short sound of **oo** as in **wool**.

wool

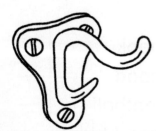  

McGraw-Hill School Division

A Good Surprise, After All

by Robin Bloksberg
illustrated by Leanne Mebust

Happy Birthday

Happy Birthday, Mom

It turned out to be a fun party after all. Mom said I was a good cook. She was happy with her flowers.
Some day I will plan another surprise party, but not for a long time!

 Helping at Home Your child has read this book in school. Have him or her read it aloud to you. Then have your child tell the story to you in his or her own words.

8

Did you ever try to keep a secret from your Mom? I did. It was a really big occasion.

Mom's birthday was coming. Dad and I planned a surprise celebration.

2

It was almost time for the party. All the decorations were up. I put on my good dress. But oh, no! I'd forgotten to pick flowers!

I raced down by the brook to get some. My dog Pudge splashed in the brook beside me. I was soaked!

Just then Mom came back! Dad and I were as surprised as she was.

7

First, Dad took me to the bookstore. I took a look at all the cookbooks and got a book of party recipes.

Then I looked out. There was Mom! I stood in back of a big wooden shelf so she didn't see me. That was close!

On the big day, Grandma Midge took Mom shopping. Dad and I raced to start cooking—white cake with fudge frosting! Oh, no! The car didn't start.

Luckily, Grandma Midge is good at fixing cars. She looked under the hood, shook a wire, and off they went.

4

The next day was even worse! Mom and I were shopping. I was thinking about the party and not paying attention to where I was going. Suddenly, I ran the cart over a man's foot. Good thing he had on thick, wool socks!

I looked up and saw that he was Dad's pal. He started to talk about the party. I gave him a nudge and a funny look. I think he understood the hint. Boy, it's hard to keep surprises from mothers.

5

oo

Name _____

Color the pictures whose names
have the short sound of **oo** as in **brook**.
Write **oo**.

brook

1.	**2.**	**3.**	**4.**
5.	**6.**	**7.**	**8.**

 Helping at Home Guide your child in creating sentences out loud containing *oo* words. For
example, "Ana took a good book to the brook." Possible words for sentences: *hood, foot, wood, hook,
cook, look, shook, football, cookbook, took, crook, wool, stood, good, soot, brook, bookstore, good-bye.*

Name _____

Circle the word that names each picture.

1.

shook   (book)

2.

judge   ledge

3.

cellar   collar

4.

vision   visor

5.

gerbil   garden

6.

station   nation

7.

sky   key

8.

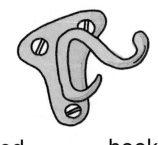

hood   hook

9.

calendar   celery

McGraw-Hill School Division

 Helping at Home Practice the sounds your child has learned by playing "Go Fish." Write each of the 18 words on this page on two individual index cards. Deal out six cards each, and match cards from each other's hand or pick from the deck. The player with the most matched cards wins.

long OO

too	zoo	moon	noon	soon
spoon	cool	pool	fool	tool
stool	boot	hoot	roof	proof
room	boom	bloom	broom	food
loose	moose	goose	loop	stoop
swoop	goofy	choose	smooth	oops
whoops	tooth	zoom	balloon	afternoon

OO

Name _____

Write **oo**. Color each picture whose name has the long sound of **oo** as in **food**.

food

Helping at Home To help your child practice the long *oo* sound, play a zoo game. Ask your child to name things that he or she might see at the zoo that have the long *oo* sound. Some examples include: a moose, a goose, a baboon, a zookeeper with a broom, balloons, and a food stand.

Introducing long *oo*

Sun and Moon

An African Tale

retold by Cheyenne Cisco
illustrated by Donna Perrone

Moon looked at Sun.
Sun looked at Moon.
Together they went up, up, up.
Sun and Moon liked their home. Their happy faces lit up the sky.
"And if Sea wants to visit," said Moon, "there is plenty of room!"

 Helping at Home Your child has read this book. Help him or her read it aloud to you. Then have your child tell you how Sun and Moon got their new home in the sky.

8

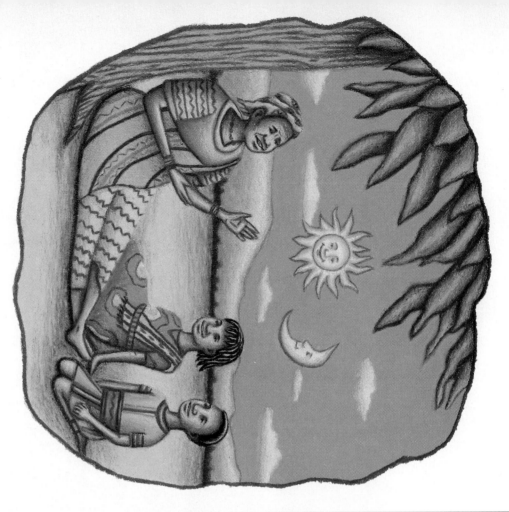

Once Sun and Moon lived in a home on the land. Just like you. Just like me. Then a friend came to visit, and they needed more room.

Let me tell you what happened.

2

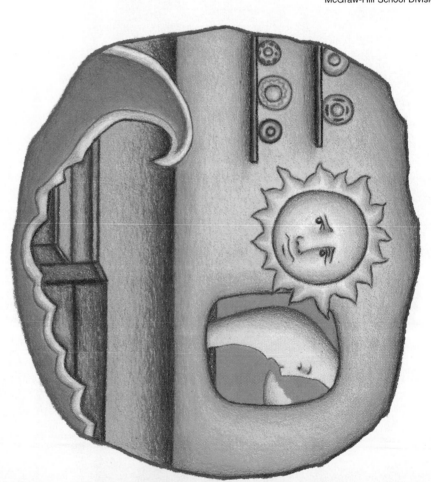

Sun and Moon ran up the steps to another room. But still the water was getting deeper and deeper.

"What can we do?" asked Moon.

"Get on the roof," said Sun.

But Sea was filling the town. Soon it reached the roof, too.

7

Sun had a best friend—Sea. They met where the beach roses bloom.

"Why don't you come to my home for lunch soon?" asked Sun. "Moon wants to see you, too."

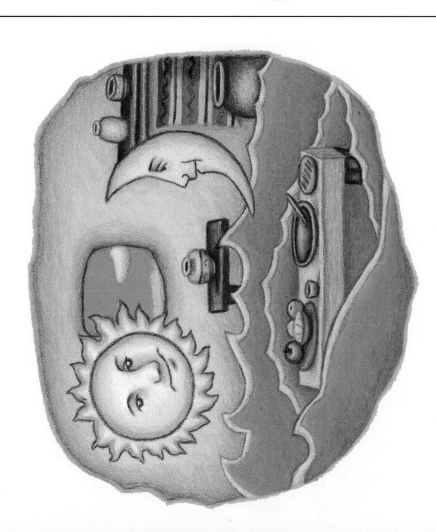

Moon served their best food. He tried to smile. But more and more water filled the room. Soon it was up over Moon's boots.

Moon looked at Sun.
Sun looked at Moon.
They got up on stools.
But Sea had a very big family. By noon, the water was over the stools, too.

4

"I don't know," Sea boomed. "I'm so big. Is there room for me?"

Sun didn't stop to think. "Just come," she said. "We'll have good food and cool drinks. Come about noon. Bring your family, too, if you choose."

So Sea went to visit his friends, Sun and Moon. His family came, too. In they went.

Soon a pool of water filled the room. Moon looked at Sun. Sun looked at Moon. They put on water-proof boots.

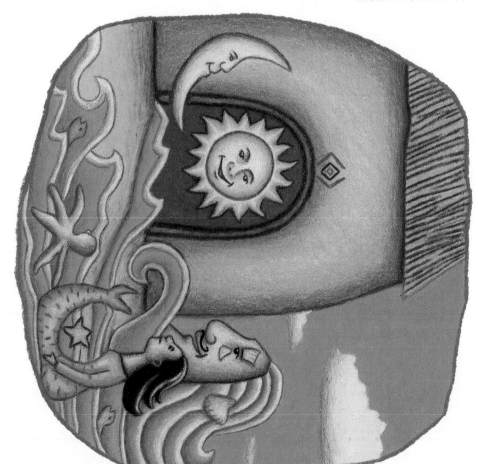

5

OO

Name _____

Choose the word that completes the sentence. Write the word.

noon	zoo	roof	balloon	tooth

1. Today I ate lunch at __noon__.

2. I can make the _____ very big.

3. A tree hit the _____.

4. My _____ is loose.

5. I went to the _____ to see the giraffes.

Helping at Home Go on a treasure hunt for items whose names contain long *oo*. Things you might find are: a cool drink, a room, a spoon, a pool, a roof, the moon, a balloon, a tool, a boot, a blooming flower, a stuffed moose or goose, a loop in a string or rope, food, a stool, a broom, a stoop.

Name_____

Circle the word that names each picture.
Write the word.

1.  (noon) / moon	**2.**  bridge / fudge	**3.**  face / lace
noon		
4.  weed / wood	**5.**  mansion / motion	**6.**  ball / broom
7.  goose / garage	**8.**  baseball / football	**9.**  cook / took

Helping at Home Your child has learned to read words containing many different sounds. Encourage him or her to practice them by writing a letter to a friend or relative.

McGraw-Hill School Division

OW

owe	own	low	row	bow
bowl	mow	mower	snow	show
slow	flow	blow	blown	glow
grow	grown	throw	thrown	yellow
fellow	pillow	hollow	follow	swallow
elbow	shadow	window	tomorrow	marshmallow

ow

Name_____

Write **ow** under each picture whose name has the long **o** sound as in **window**. Draw lines to match the letters.

wind**ow**

1.

_____

_____

O W

2.

_____

_____

3.

_____

_____

4.

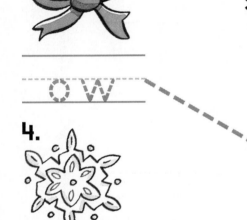

_____

_____

ow

5.

_____

_____

6.

_____

_____

7.

_____

_____

8.

_____

_____

 Helping at Home To practice the long *o* sound of *ow*, say *pillow* and emphasize the *ow* sound. Then say the words below. Have your child point to his or her elbow if the word has the *ow* sound of *pillow: fellow, fall, blowing, follow, fool, throw, bowl, through, hollow, howl, swallow, swell.*

McGraw-Hill School Division

MR. SNOW'S NEW HOME

by Jordan Swinton

illustrated by Giora Carmi

HOME SWEET HOME

Mr. Snow showed his friends everything. They went rowing on the brook. Afterwards, they sat by the glowing fire and toasted marshmallows.

They said, "You can really throw a party, Mr. Snow."

Mr. Snow grinned. "My big yellow cabin really feels like home now," he said. "Can you come back next weekend?"

Helping at Home Your child has read this book in school. Have him or her read it aloud to you. Then have your child find and write the *ow* words in the story.

8

Mr. Snow liked his friends and he liked his home in the city. But it was just too small.

Mr. Snow wanted to own a big, new home.

2

Then one day, a van was blowing its horn in Mr. Snow's driveway. It was all of his friends from the city!

Mr. Snow ran to hug them. He was one happy fellow!

7

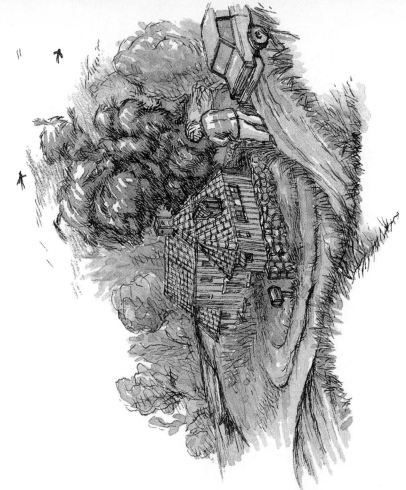

Soon he got a big yellow cabin far from the city. It had a low stone wall. A brook flowed by. A pine tree made a shadow over it.

"That's where I will sit," said Mr. Snow. "In the shade of that tree."

Mr. Snow wished he had a camera. He wanted to show his friends his new cabin.

The big yellow cabin looked a lot better. Mr. Snow liked the roses growing by the wall. He liked the swallows that nested in the hollow of his tree. He liked the ducks swimming slowly in the brook.

But the cabin still did not feel like home.

But the big yellow cabin just did not feel like home. The windows had cracks. The grass had grown up to his elbows. And someone had thrown trash in the brook.

"It needs a little fixing up," said Mr. Snow. He got going.

Mr. Snow fixed the windows so the wind did not blow in. He cleaned up the brook, and he mowed the grass.

OW

Name _____

Choose the word that completes the sentence. Write the word.

snow window showed pillow slower

1.

Fluffy was still asleep on my _pillow_.

2.

I ran to the _____ .

3.

There was _____ on the street.

4.

I _____ Ben the way.

5.

Ben went _____ than me.

Helping at Home Your child is learning the long *o* sound of *ow* as in *pillow*. Invite your child to write *ow* on a piece of paper. Say the words below. If a word has the *ow* sound of *pillow*, have your child draw a picture of it: *marshmallow, car, window, snow, bowl, lawn mower, puzzle.*

Fill in the circle in front of the word that names
each picture. Write the word.

1. ○ snow
   ● blow

blow

2. ○ wooden
   ○ woolly

3. ○ rowing
   ○ bowling

4. ○ station
   ○ state

5. ○ goose
   ○ moose

6. ○ television
   ○ window

7. ○ hedge
   ○ lodge

8. ○ gems
   ○ germs

9. ○ slice
   ○ place

Helping at Home Write the following words on cards: *engine, station, boot, hook, cellar, bridge.*
Have your child use each of the words in a sentence. Encourage him or her to combine some of the
words in the same sentence.

ou

our	sour	flour	out	bout
about	shout	count	bounce	house
blouse	mouth	south	loud	proud
cloud	pound	mound	sound	round
around	ground	hound	found	trout

ou

Name_____

Write **ou**. Color each picture whose name has the sound of **ou** as in **shout**.

shout

ou

 Helping at Home To practice the sound of *ou* as in *cloud*, write the following words on two sets of cards: *our, shout, sound, found, out*. Turn the cards face down. Have your child choose two cards and read the words aloud. If they match, your child keeps the matching pair. If they don't, it's your turn.

124   Introducing *ou*

McGraw-Hill School Division

ou

your	yours	tour		
you	soup	group		
four	fourth	pour	court	
touch	couple	country	double	trouble
young	younger	youngster	famous	

ou

Name _____

Name each picture. Draw lines to match the pictures with the same **ou** sound. Write **ou**.

1.

f _ou_ r

2.

gr____ p

3.

s____p

4.

c____ntry

5.

c____ple

6.

p___ r

 Helping at Home To practice the *ou* sounds in *four, soup,* and *couple,* write the following word pairs, each word on a separate square of paper: *four/your, soup/group, double/trouble.* Read the pairs with your child, then mix up the pieces of paper. Invite your child to match the rhyming pairs.

McGraw-Hill School Division

THE HOUND AND THE TROUT

by C. A. Gregsak

illustrated by Consuelo Udave

"I like to make my own loud sounds," the hound said. "I found out what is better for me!"

And the yellow hound howled her own big, happy howl.

 Helping at Home Your child has read this book in school. Help him or her read it to you. Then take the parts of the trout and the hound and read each character's lines.

8

A yellow hound dog came to her country house. She set her bags on the ground and ran around and about. Down at the pond, she stopped and howled. She made a loud, happy sound and lay in the shadows.

"I like to swim with the group," said the trout. "I like to make round bubbles. I like to make a low, quiet sound. The pond is better for me."

A group of trout swam around in the pond. One trout looked up at the hound. Four round bubbles rose from his mouth. "What a fine, loud sound you make!" said the trout. "I want to be out of the water like you. I want to run on the ground by myself. I want to be loud. Your way is better. I'm getting out of here!" said the trout.

"I am in big trouble!" said the hound. And she got out of the pond. "I am in big trouble!" said the trout, and he flopped back into the pond.

The hound looked at the trout. "I think there is more fun to be found in the water," she said.

"I want to swim around and around with a group of trout like you," the hound said. "I want to blow four round bubbles. I want to make a low, quiet sound."

"Your way is better. I'm going in!" said the hound.

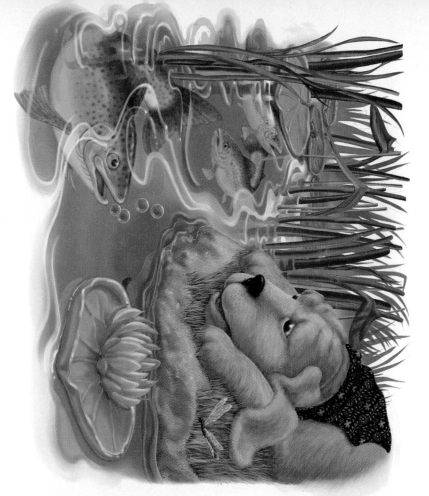

Out jumped the trout! He hit the ground. Flip, flop, flip! He bounced around. In went the hound. Flip, flop, splash! She tried to blow bubbles, but not one came out.

ou

Color the pictures whose names have the sound of **ou** as in **ground**. Write **ou**.

ground

1. 	**2.** 

_____ _____

ou

3. 	**4.** 

_____ _____

5.	**6.** 

_____ _____

7. 	**8.** 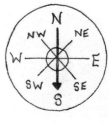

_____ _____

Helping at Home Your child is learning to recognize words that have the *ou* sound as in *house*. Write the following on pieces of paper: *hound, found, proud, sour, about, loud*. Take turns picking a piece of paper, reading the word, and using it in a sentence.

ou

Name_____

Choose the word that completes
the sentence. Write the word.

| Country | trouble | group | tour | touch |

1.

We took a ___tour___ of the White House.

2.

There was a _____ from our class.

3.

I wanted to _____ the desk.

4.

I did not want to get into _____ .

5.

This man is called the "Father of Our _____ ."

 Helping at Home Your child is learning words with the *ou* sounds as in *four, soup,* and *couple.*
To help your child practice, write the following on a piece of paper in large letters: y_ _, y_ _rs,
y_ _ nger, t_ _ ch, tr_ _ ble. Invite your child to write *ou* on the blank lines, then read each word.

McGraw-Hill School Division

Name_____

Circle the missing letters. Then write them.
Read the word.

1.

4

ow

(ou)

f _ou_ r

2.

oo

ou

f __ __ t

3.

ou

ow

sn __ __

4.

oo

ou

sp __ __ n

5.

dge

g

bri __ __

6.

ton

tion

lo __ __

Helping at Home Your child can read and write words with many vowel sounds. Play "I Spy" around your home, pointing out the following items and inviting your child to say and write the words: *broom, soup, blouse, hook, lotion, collar, plant, wire, toes, coat,* the number *four* (on a clock).

Name_____

Circle the word that names each picture.
Write the word.

1.
hour

(house)

house

2.
shadow

window

_____

3.
cloud

crowd

_____

4.
spoon

moon

_____

5.
addition

motion

_____

6.
pour

pout

_____

7.
boot

book

_____

8.
bowl

howl

_____

9.
soup

soot

_____

Helping at Home Encourage your child to practice some of the new words he or she has learned by thinking of make-believe things sold at the "Silly Store." Have your child draw and label such items as pet clouds, sparkle spray, and dancing televisions.

McGraw-Hill School Division

u
u_e

utensil	usual	uniform	unite	music
museum	bugle	super	Judy	
use	cube	tube	tune	
prune	cute	flute	rude	
rule	huge	perfume	costume	
duke	lute	June	Bruce	
pure	cure	future	secure	

u

Name _____

Write **u** under each picture whose name has the long **u** sound as in **bugle**. Draw lines to match the letters.

bugle

1.
_____
_ _ _ u _ _ _

2.
_____
_____

3.
_____
_____

4.
_____
_ _ _ _ _ _ _

u

5.
_____
_ _ _ _ _ _ _

6.
_____
_ _ _ _ _ _ _

7.
_____
_____

8.
_____
_____

McGraw-Hill School Division

 Helping at Home To help your child practice the long *u* sound as in *bugle*, write the following words on a piece of paper: *utensil, music, museum, unite, uniform.* Take turns reading each word, emphasizing the long *u* sound.

Introducing long *u*

u_e

Name _____

Circle the pictures whose names have the long **u** sound as in **flute**. Write **u** and **e**.

flute

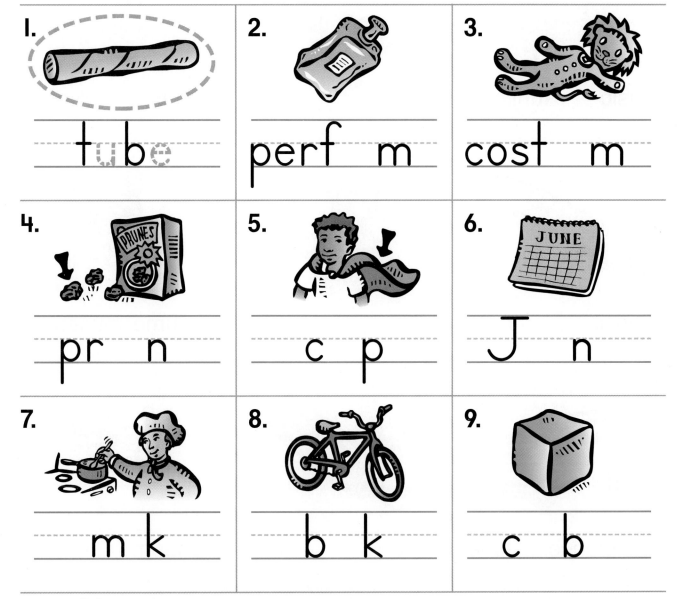

1. t u b e

2. perf __ m

3. cost __ m

4. pr __ n

5. c __ p

6. J __ n

7. __ m __ k

8. b __ k

9. c __ b

 Helping at Home To help your child practice the long *u* sound, write *rule* and *cute* at the top a piece of paper. Help your child to write a list of household rules and a list of things that are cute, beneath the appropriate word.

u
u __ e

Circle the word that names each picture.

1.

music   (uniform)

2.

flute   float

3.

perfume   proof

4.

utensil   ruler

5.

tube   bugle

6.

costume   museum

7.

ambulance   tune

8.

flute   tube

9.

museum   music

 Helping at Home Your child has been learning words with long *u*. Write the following words on paper: *museum, music, bugle, flute, costume, tune, uniform, perfume*. Challenge your child to use these words in a story about a trip to a museum or a concert.

WHAT DID JUDY SEE?

by Stephanie Hurley

illustrated by Alex Bloch

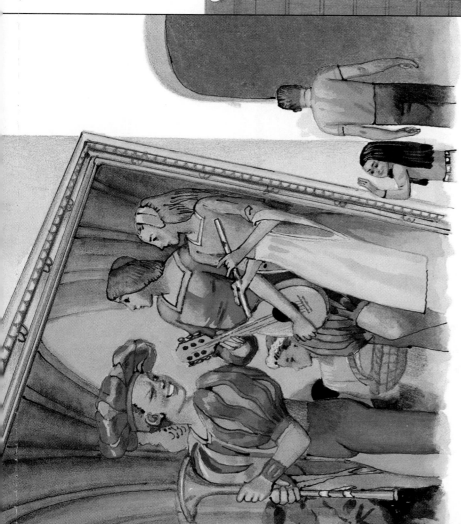

Just then Judy's father called her. "Let's go," he said. "We can't use up all our time in this room. This museum is huge. There's lots more to see."

Judy stood up and looked at the painting. She waved good-bye to the boy.

 Helping at Home Your child has read this book. Read it together. Then ask your child to tell how he or she would feel to see a picture come alive.

It was Judy's first trip to the art museum.

"Wow," she said as she looked around.

She patted a stone cat. "How cute!" she said.

A man in a uniform came up to her.

"Please do not touch the art," he said.

"Sorry, that is the rule."

McGraw-Hill School Division

BUMP!

Judy bumped into the man in the uniform.

"Those kids are good dancers," she said.

"What kids?" asked the man.

"You'll find lots to look at in here," said the man in uniform. He led Judy to the next room.

There on the wall was a huge picture. Judy stared and stared. "It looks so real!" she said. She began to daydream.

Just then the duke and his lady came in. Girls tossed roses at their feet. Judy smelled the sweet flowers. A lady with a flute and a man with a lute played a tune. The girls danced to the music.

Judy started to dance, too. Then she jumped to catch a rose.

"What do you use that for?" she asked
the cute boy in the painting.

"It's a bugle," he said. "You can make
music with it."

"Will you show me how to play your
bugle?" asked Judy.

The boy played a little tune. The sound
was pure and clear.

Name _____

Choose the word that completes
the sentence. Write the word.

| super   bugle   museum   music   uniform |

1. The scout looked proud in his _uniform_.

2. Genna played a _____ in the band.

3. We saw moon rocks at the _____ .

4. We had a _____ time on the swings.

5. Flute _____ is nice and soft.

Helping at Home You can help your child with words that have the long *u* sound by playing cha-rades. Invite him or her to write the following words on slips of paper: *music, bugle, super hero, truth, museum.* Take turns picking a word and acting it out while the other person guesses it.

u __ e

Name _____

Circle the word that names each picture.
Write the word.

1. huge (circled) / hog

huge

2. prune / run

_____

3. tube / tape

_____

4. perform / perfume

_____

5. flutter / flute

_____

6. dune / dance

_____

7. tune / tunnel

_____

8. cute / cube

_____

9. perfume / costume

_____

Helping at Home Your child is learning words that have the long *u* sound as in *flute* and *cube*. Have your child write the following words: *June, flute, use, tune, huge, cute, rule*. Challenge your child to use as many of the words as he or she can in a single sentence.

Circle the word that names each picture.

1.

(flute)   flower

2.

window   windmill

3.

group   rope

4.

bugle   bounce

5.

tour   tube

6.

foot   four

7.

mouth   mellow

8.

spoon   soup

9.

vision   invention

 Helping at Home Write the following words on a piece of paper: *soup, window, ruler, flower, cute, tube, perfume, uniform.* With your child, go on a treasure hunt in which he or she tries to find an example of as many of these words as possible.

Fill in the circle in front of the missing letters.
Then write them. Read the word.

1.

○ oo

● ow

holl_ow_

2.

○ ow

○ ee

b_____

3.

○ oo

○ ai

p____l

4.

○ e

○ u

m____sic

5.

○ ai

○ oo

m____n

6.

○ o

○ u

____niform

 Helping at Home Make "Silly Sound Soup." Draw a big soup pot on paper and ask your child to draw ingredients inside the pot. Drawings may include only items with the sound of *u*, *u*-consonant-*e*, *ou*, *ow*, and *oo*. Examples: a crescent moon, a lawn mower, a yellow balloon, a flute, a cloud.

McGraw-Hill School Division

ue
ui

due	Sue	blue	clue
glue	glued	true	Tuesday
suit	fruit	juice	juicy
bruise	cruise	cruised	suitcase

Name _____

ue

Write **ue** under each picture whose name has the sound of **ue** as in **Sue.** Draw lines to match the letters.

Sue

1.

~~ue~~

2.

3.

4.

ue

5.

6.

7.

8.

 Helping at Home To help your child practice the long *u* sound as in *blue*, invite him or her to write the following words on a piece of paper: *due, blue, glue, clue, true*. Have your child use each word in a sentence.

McGraw-Hill School Division

Name _____

ui

Write **ui**. Color each picture whose name has the sound of **ui** as in **suit**.

suit

_____

ui

Helping at Home To practice the *ui* sound in *suitcase*, write the following words on paper: *cruise, suitcase, suit, swimsuit, fruit, fruitcake, juice*. Have your child read each word, then imagine going on a cruise. Which of the items would he or she bring along? What else would your child bring?

Introducing /ü/ *ui*   149

Name _____

Circle the word that names each picture.

1. June   (juice)

2. blue   bill

3. cruise   circus

4. glue   blue

5. suitcase   sugar

6. suit   fruit

7. true   suit

8. clue   clay

9. dune   due

Helping at Home Your child is learning to read and spell words with *ue* and *ui*. To practice, help your child make a paper collage of fruit inside a big blue bowl. On the blue bowl, have your child write as many words as he or she can think of with *ue*. Then write *ui* words on the pieces of fruit.

The Case of the Missing Fruit

by Dona McDuff

illustrated by Terry Kovalcik

We checked the deer pen. No fruit. No clues.

We went to the pandas. No fruit. No clues.

We went past the birds. Same thing. No fruit. No clues.

Then we came to the monkey cage.

Helping at Home Your child has read this book in school. Help him or her read it aloud to you. Then have your child tell what happened to the missing fruit in the story.

8

It all started when we voted on where to go for our class trip.

The boat cruise got five votes and the museum trip got one. The zoo trip got ten votes.

"True, blue, and cool!" said Julio.

"We're going to the zoo!" He liked to say things like that.

McGraw-Hill School Division

"Hey," said Sue. "My fruit is missing!"

"That's strange," I said. "My apple is gone, too."

Hmmm... We had a problem. Lots of kids had fruit missing. It was true.

"We'll have to look for clues," said Miss Bruce.

"We'll go on the first Tuesday in June," said Miss Bruce.

Then she said, "Bring lots of food. Pack some juice and fruit for snacks."

"I'll need my blue backpack to carry all that!" said Sue.

"True!" said Julio. "I think I'll bring a suitcase!"

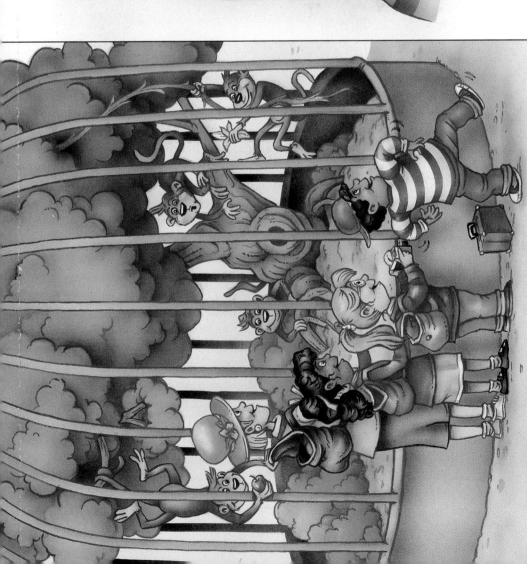

At last we came to the best part of the zoo, the monkeys.

"Look at how the monkey is trying to take away that banana!" said Sue.

"Time for lunch!" called Miss Bruce.

When Tuesday came, Miss Bruce wore her big blue hat. She said it was to help us see and follow her.

We made up a silly song: "99 bottles of juice on the bus, 99 bottles of juice! Take one down and pass it around, 98 bottles of juice on the bus."

At the zoo a man in a uniform met us. First he took us to see the deer. A little deer was stuck to its mother like glue. Then he led us to see the pandas. Julio said that they had on suits!

"That's not true," said Sue.

Then we saw some wild birds swoop down to pick up some fruit. Whoosh!

"Wow!" said Julio.

ue ui

Circle the word that completes the sentence.
Write the word.

1. These books are ___due___ today.

dune

(due)

moon

2. The chair needs _____.

gloom

clue

glue

3. I like _____ with my eggs.

juice

prunes

suits

4. The sky is _____.

blue

bruise

clue

5. Apples and peaches are _____.

spoon

blue

fruit

Helping at Home To help your child become familiar with words that have the long *u* sound of *ui* and *ue*, write the following words on a piece of paper: *true, juice, blue, suitcase, glue, bruise, due.* Together, make up silly sentences using these words.

| ue |
| ui |

Name_____

Choose the word that completes
the sentence. Write the word.

| bruised | clue | Sue | suit | suitcase |

1.

Mom dresses for work in a _____ suit _____ .

2.

He gave the book to _____ .

3.

Jan fell and _____ her leg.

4.

The _____ is too full to close.

5.

She found a _____ .

McGraw-Hill School Division

Helping at Home Your child is learning words that have the *ui* and *ue* sound as in *suitcase* and *clue*. Help him or her by saying the following pairs of words aloud. Have your child tell you which word has the *ui* or *ue* sound in each pair: *finish/fruit, juice/cheek, chirp/cruise, scare/suit, glue/glare, bill/blue.*

Name _____

Circle the word that names each picture.

1. elk (elbow)

2. costume cruise

3. bruise rude

4. tooth tube

5. glue flute

6. cube cute

7. bounce broom

8. room throw

9. jump juice

 Helping at Home Help your child write a journal entry each Tuesday for one month, using as many *ue*, *ui*, *u*, *u*-consonant-*e*, and *ou* words as possible. Some of the following words may be easily incorporated into your child's journal: *use*, *soup*, *music*, *super*, *blue*, *true*, *young*, *fruit*, *juice*.

Name_____

Circle the word that names each picture.
Write the word.

1.

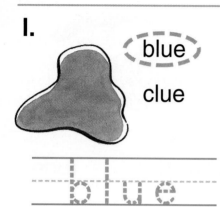

(blue)

clue

b l u e

2.

house

mouse

_____

3.

suit

fruit

_____

4.

spool

spoon

_____

5.

plate

prune

_____

6.

food

foot

_____

7.

bounce

bowl

_____

8.

music

museum

_____

9.

perfume

pond

_____

Helping at Home Help your child identify vowel sounds in words by pointing out the following objects around the house: a *couch, table, suitcase, lamp, sink, window, utensils, tube, ruler, glue, juice, food, stool, broom.* Help your child write down each item and circle the vowel sounds in each word.

oi
oy

oil	boil	soil	foil
broil	spoil	voice	choice
coin	join	joint	point
noise	noisy	moist	moisture
boy	toy	joy	enjoy
annoy	loyal	royal	oyster
Roy			

oi
oy

Name_____

Color each picture whose name has the same vowel sound as in **joint** and **toy**.

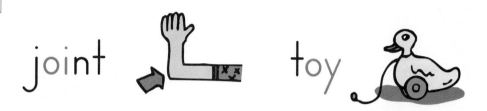

joint   toy

McGraw-Hill School Division

Helping at Home Write the following words: *oil, boil, foil, toy, boy, royal, voice, coin.* Have your child create a superhero, using as many *oi* and *oy* words as possible. For example, Clean Choice. She cleans up the oil in the seas and chemicals in the soil. Royal Boy. He foils bad guys with toys.

Name _____

Circle the word that names each picture.
Write the word.

foil   cowboy

---

1.  (joints)

   jeans

   joints

2. coin

   coil

   ____

3. master

   oyster

   ____

4. bow

   boy

   ____

5. royal

   round

   ____

6. point

   paint

   ____

7. sell

   soil

   ____

8. toys

   tail

   ____

9. lost

   joy

   ____

 Helping at Home Have your child use the point of a pen to write words on aluminum foil. Use such picturable words as *boy, toy, royal, oil, soil,* and *coin.* Have your child draw a picture to go with each word and then trace each word with his or her finger.

oi
oy

Name _____

Circle the word that completes
the sentence. Write the word.

1.

The duck ___decoy___ is brown.

enjoy
annoy
(decoy)

2.

He wants to _____ them.

joy
join
coin

3.

A boy scout is _____ .

loan
loyal
royal

4.

We can shape _____ sand.

moist
mast
mist

5.

Her _____ is quiet.

choice
joint
voice

 Helping at Home   To help your child become familiar with the *oi* and *oy* sound as in *join* and *boy*, challenge him or her to write a short rhyming poem using the words *boy, toy* and *joy; royal* and *loyal; choice* and *voice;* or *oil, foil,* and *soil.*

COOKING WITH ROY

by Susan McCloskey

illustrated by Ilja Bereznickas

Well, boys and girls, I'm hungry for a snack. I wish you could join me! If you hear a lot of noise, it's only me enjoying the Peanut Bars. So long!

 Helping at Home Your child has read this book in school. Have him or her read it aloud to you. Then invite your child to tell how to make his or her favorite sandwich.

8

2

Hello, boys and girls! I'm glad you could join me for "Cooking with Roy." Like all cooks, I enjoy making good things to eat. I'll bet you do, too.

McGraw-Hill School Division

Cut the Peanut Bars into squares—about 24.

Just have some foil handy to cover them. The foil will keep them moist and crunchy.

7

Today I'll show you how to make some tasty Peanut Bars. The best thing is that you don't have to bake them. And you don't have to boil, broil, or fry them.

In fact, you don't have to cook them at all. You just have to mix them, eat them, and enjoy them!

COOKING WITH ROY

Stir in a cup of peanut butter—creamy or crunchy. It's your choice. If you want, add a cup of cut-up apple, too.

Now stir in 5 cups of oat cereal. Whoops! Be careful not to spill it!

Now press the batter into the pan. Put some oil on your hands to keep the Peanut Bars from sticking.

Start by putting a little oil on the inside of the pan. The oil keeps the Peanut Bars from sticking. The pan I'm using is 13 inches long and 9 inches wide. Next, put three tablespoons of soft butter in a big bowl.

McGraw-Hill School Division

Add 2 cups of marshmallow fluff to the bowl. With a spoon, stir the marshmallow and the butter until they are mixed well.

oi
oy

Name _____

Circle the word that names each picture.

1. soil   sail

2. spoil   point

3. oyster   oil

4. toy   foil

5. boy   annoy

6. rays   royal

7. coins   chains

8. toil   oil

9. boil   broil

oi
oy

Choose the word that completes
the sentence. Write the word.

| choice | oyster | noise | enjoy | annoy |

1.

They _____enjoy_____ working with clay.

2.

Do not make any _____ .

3.

Loud noises_____ him.

4.

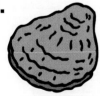

The _____ lives in a shell.

5.

It is hard to make a _____ .

Helping at Home Practice listening for the sound of *oy* and *oi* in words at the dinner table tonight.
Agree on five "whoops words," such as *boy, toy, enjoy, noise,* and *boil* that nobody can say during the
meal. Ask each other questions to trick each other into accidentally saying those "whoops words."

McGraw-Hill School Division

Circle the missing letters. Then write them.
Read the word.

1. oy
ou

dec**oy**

2. ir
oo

sc____p

3. ou
o

cl____ds

4. ey
oy

b____

5. oi
ui

c____ns

6. oy
ou

c____ntry

 Helping at Home To help your child review the words that he or she has learned so far, suggest that he or she create a comic strip. Have your child invent funny characters and make up a story about them. Remind him or her to write what the characters say in speech bubbles.

Name_____

Choose the missing letters from the box to complete each word. Write the letters. Read each word.

| oo | l | ue | ui | ou | fl |

1.

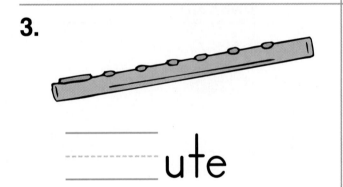

bl_ue_

2.

z_____

3.

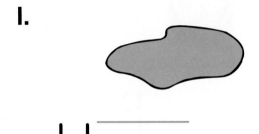

_____ute

4.

oi_____

5.

fr_____t

6.

s_____p

McGraw-Hill School Division

ew
eau

new	few	dew	chew
grew	flew	drew	crew
stew	blew	threw	screw
beauty	beautiful		

ew
eau

Name_____

Color each picture whose name has the long **u** sound as in **new** and **beautiful**.

new   beautiful

MABEL'S

The TIMES

Helping at Home Your child is learning to read and spell words with *ew* and *eau*. To practice, make up a silly story about a beauty contest held by cows on a ship. The contestants include the ship's crew. Use some of the following words: *beautiful, blew, chew, few, grew, new, threw*.

Introducing *ew, eau*

What Grew in My Garden

by Linda Yoshizawa
illustrated by Jenny Vainisi

Then summer rain fell.
More breezes blew.
There was one more
thing that was new.
That bug grew up.
And then it flew.

Isn't it a beauty?

 Helping at Home Your child has read this book in school. Have him or her read it aloud to you. Then have your child write sentences about some of the things in the garden.

8

Step into my garden.
Come and see what's new.
I dug the dirt
and planted seeds.
I watered them
and pulled the weeds.
And this is what I grew.
What a beautiful !

McGraw-Hill School Division

Step into my garden.
Come and see what's new.
I think it's odd.
Do you think so, too?
I did not plant this.
Just watch it chew!
What do you think this bug will do?
What a beautiful !

Step into my garden.
Come and see what's new.
Some plants are nice
to sniff and see.
A few call out to honeybees.
And some are nice to chew.

What a beautiful  !

Step into my garden.
Come and see what's new.
The sun shines down
on silver dew.
Soft summer breezes
blow and blow.
And here are the flowers that grow.

What a beautiful  !

Step into my garden.
Come and see what's new.
Now I have all
the plants I need.
But a bird flew by
and dropped a seed.
And here's the plant that grew.

What a beautiful  **!**

4

McGraw-Hill School Division

Step into my garden.
Come and see what's new.
I plan to pick
a few of these,
add chewy meat,
some beans and peas,
and make a pot of stew.

What a beautiful **!**

5

ew

eau

Circle the word that names each picture.

I. new ~~(circled)~~   now

2. grew   gown

3. stew   slew

4. screws   straws

5. new   newspaper

6. beauty   blew

7. clue   few

8. chew   threw

9. beauty   beads

 Helping at Home Encourage your child to make up silly sentences using words with the long *u* sound of *ew* and *eau*. Examples: He threw the newspaper into the stew. He drew a beautiful screwdriver.

Name_____

Fill in the circle in front of the missing letters.
Then write them. Read the word.

1.
● ew
○ ly

f _ew_

2.
○ oo
○ eau

b _____ ty

3.
○ ee
○ ew

thr _____

4.
○ u
○ o

t _____ ba

5.
○ oi
○ eu

n _____ se

6.
○ ew
○ oy

scr _____

Helping at Home Suggest that your child create a map. This map can be of your neighborhood,
a favorite place away from home, a treasure map, or a map of an imaginary place. Have him or her
write street names, building signs, and directions to practice reading and writing many new words.

McGraw-Hill School Division

aw
au

saw	paw	raw	law	jaw
claw	straw	yawn	fawn	lawn
dawn	hawk	crawl	shawl	awful
pause	cause	because	sauce	saucer
sausage	haunt	fault	cautiously	somersault

aw

Name _____

Color the pictures whose names have the sound of **aw** as in **lawn**. Write **aw**.

lawn

1.

_____
aw

2.

_____

3.

_____

4.

_____

5.

_____

6.

_____

7.

_____

8.

_____

 Helping at Home To help your child learn the *aw* sound as in *jaw*, play ten questions. One of you thinks of a word such as *hawk* or *dawn* that has the *aw* sound. The other asks questions that require a "yes" or "no" answer. Try to guess the word before ten questions have been asked.

McGraw-Hill School Division

au

Name_____

Write **au** under each picture whose name has the sound of **au** as in **caution**. Draw lines to match the letters.

caution

1.

au

2.

3.

4.

au

5.

6.

7.

8.

 Helping at Home Write *au* words such as *sausage, sauce, astronaut, faucet, because, pause, fault* on cards. Place a large saucer on the floor and have your child try to toss the cards in the saucer. Ask him or her to read each card in the saucer.

Name_____

Circle the word that names each picture.

1.

(saucer)   soil

2.

claw   cloud

3.

law   lawn

4.

crawl   somersault

5.

sausage   fruit

6.

pause   paw

7.

shawl   lawn

8.

few   fawn

9.

sauce   saw

Helping at Home Encourage your child to practice words with *au* and *aw* by writing poems or rhyming couplets. Possible rhyming words: *saw/jaw, law/paw, because/pause, shawl/crawl, dawn/lawn/fawn.*

Up at Dawn

by Anne W. Phillips
illustrated by Makiko Nagano

Soon I will go back inside.
Grandma will fix some
toast, and cereal, and sausage.
But not yet,
because she likes to pause
every morning, too,
and help me watch the dawn.

 Helping at Home Your child has read this book. Take turns reading it aloud. Then have your child write some of the words in the story that have the /ô/ sound, as in dawn.

It is dawn.
I look out my window.
A deer and her fawn
come out from the trees
and onto the lawn.
They pause to nibble the straw
I hauled from the barn
and left for them to eat.

2

I wrap myself in Grandma's shawl
and softly step outside.
The grass is wet on my bare feet.
The air is cool,
and the sky is yellow.
Each dawn the world feels brand new.

2

7

My cat comes home
on silent paws.
He drinks from the saucer of milk
I left for him.
Then he crawls into the box
I filled with soft rags
and put by the steps for him to sleep in.

Sometimes when I wake up
I'm still sleepy.
I yawn because I am tired,
but I don't go back to bed.

4

Sparrows make an awful racket
in their nest under the awning
of my window.
Five eggs hatched.
I pause to watch the parent birds
feeding worms
to all the hungry baby birds.

A hawk circles in the sky at dawn.
It lands in a tall pine tree
and curls its claws around a branch.

5

aw

Name _____

Circle the pictures whose names have the sound of **aw** as in **hawk**. Write **aw**.

hawk

1. (circled picture) _____ aw	**2.** _____	**3.** _____
4. _____	**5.** _____	**6.** _____
7. _____	**8.** _____	**9.** _____

 Helping at Home Challenge your child to list ten words that have the *aw* sound. Some of the words on his or her list might be: *awful, awning, raw, saw, law, jaw, paw, claw, yawn, fawn, lawn, dawn, hawk, straw, crawl,* and *shawl.*

au

Name _____

Choose the word that completes the sentence.
Write the word.

| because | caution | haul | saucer | sausage |

1.

Tim was in bed  because he was sick.

2.

Do you eat _____ with your eggs?

3.

Use _____ when you cross the street.

4.

A mule can _____ a big load.

5.

The cup and _____ match.

 Helping at Home To practice words with *au*, cut out a paper ice cream cone. Have your child think of zany ice cream flavors such as spicy sausage and tomato sauce! Have your child write the crazy flavors on paper scoops of ice cream and tape them to the cone.

Practicing /ô/ *au*

McGraw-Hill School Division

Name_____

Circle the missing letters. Then write them.
Read the word.

1.

oi

(aw)

_____

y aw n

2.

oi

u

_____

v_____ce

3.

ou

ui

_____

m_____th

4.

au

ay

_____

s_____ce

5.

ai

aw

_____

str_____

6.

aw

ue

_____

bl_____

 Helping at Home Have your child make a dictionary to record words that he or she is learning or often uses in writing. Bind a small book that has one or two pages for each letter in the alphabet. Encourage him or her to illustrate those words that are difficult to read or remember.

Name_____

Choose the missing letters from the box to complete each word. Write the letters. Read each word.

ew	oi	sh	aw	eau	au

1.

scr<u>ew</u>driver

2.

b_____ty

3.

f____n

4.

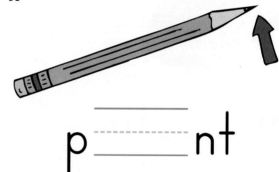

p____nt

5.

s____ce

6.

____awl

Helping at Home Place assorted articles of oversized clothing such as a *skirt, shirt, blouse, shorts,* and *shawl* in a basket. Have your child choose one item and spell it. If spelled correctly, your child puts on the item. Be sure to take a picture of your child at the end.

ph
gh

photo	photograph	phone	telephone
phrase	pharmacy	alphabet	elephant
nephew	orphan	autograph	microphone
laugh	laughter		

Name_____

Color the pictures whose names have the same sound of **f** as in **phone** and **laugh**.

pone

lau

The Elephants Come Back

by Kana Riley

illustrated by Stephanie O'Shaughnessy

"Wow!" I said. "Not bad for an old group!" I even started to sing "Ha–ha–ha–HA!" Mom and Jane looked at me and laughed.

"Pretty good for a kid!" they said.

"Can we get their autographs after the show?" I begged. "Please?"

8

"Jess," cried Mom. "The Elephants are coming!"

She hung up the phone and ran to tell me the news.

"Jane's nephew gave her three concert tickets. You can come, too!"

You see, when Mom and Jane were kids, they loved this band called the Elephants. Now Mom was really excited. Me? I wasn't so sure. Would I like that old band?

McGraw-Hill School Division

Mom and Jane could hardly sit still. Just then a man stepped up to the microphone.

"And now, the band you have waited twenty years for—the Elephants!"

Mom and Jane stood up and cheered.

The Elephants began to play. "You make me laugh," they sang. Everyone roared back the phrase, "Ha—ha—ha—HA!"

"Come up to the attic," said Mom. She pulled out her photograph album. "Look," she said, pointing to a photo.

"That's Jane and me when we got the Elephants' autograph! Whatever happened to that? Let's see if it's here." We hunted around in the trunk. No autograph.

All week long, Mom was excited. On Tuesday we went to Phillips Pharmacy to get a roll of film. "We have to take lots of photos," she said.

She was always on the telephone with Jane. They kept remembering stuff from the old days and laughing.

Me? I was getting a little excited, too. By the day of the concert, I couldn't wait to go.

4

We did find some cool things. Too small for Mom. And too big for me. They gave us a good laugh.

McGraw-Hill School Division

Mom got out her old tapes. "Listen to this," she said. She started to play "You Make Me Laugh." Then she did these funny dance steps. Every time the Elephants sang the phrase, "You make me laugh," Mom would bend over and sing, "Ha—ha—ha—HA!"

5

ph
gh

Name _____

Choose the word that completes
the sentence. Write the word.

laugh autograph elephant photo Dolphins

1.  The mayor gave me his _autograph_ .

2.  _____ are very smart.

3.  The _____ likes to eat peanuts.

4.  Dad takes our _____ at the zoo.

5.  Grandpa makes me _____ .

 Helping at Home Draw a paper target with three rings. Write 5-point words: *photo* and *phone* in the outer ring; 10-point words: *phrase* and *laugh* in the middle ring; 50-point words: *pharmacy* and *microphone* in the center. Flip pennies onto the target, read the words, and count the score.

Name_____

Circle the missing letters. Then write them. Read the word.

1. 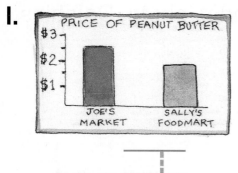 pe

(ph)

gra**ph**

2.  ph

v

____ one

3.  au

ou

l____ nch

4. au

aw

oi

cr____ l

5.  aw

ew

st____

6.  th

ph

____ oto

 Helping at Home Challenge your child to use his or her growing knowledge of words. Place a three syllable word such as *microphone* at the top of a sheet of paper. How many new words can your child make using the letters in *microphone*?

Cumulative Review

ch

echo	ache	anchor	school	mechanic
chord	chorus	chrome	character	chemistry
stomach	orchestra	mechanical		

chef	Chicago	chute	parachute	machine
machinery				

ch

Name _____

Name each picture. Draw a line to the **chorus** if the name has the sound of **k**.
Draw a line to the **chef** if the name has the sound of **sh**.

chorus   chef

 Helping at Home Say these words: *chorus, chute, echo, school, machine, parachute, mechanic, charades, anchor, orchestra*. If your child hears the sound of *ch* as in *stomach*, he or she pats his or her stomach. If your child hears the sound of *ch* as in *chef*, he or she pretends to be stirring a fancy sauce.

silent w

| write | wrote | wrap | wrapper | wrist |
| wring | wrong | wreck | wrinkle | writer |

silent w

Name_____

Circle the pictures whose names begin with **wr** as in **wrinkle**. Write **wr**.

wrinkle

I. _____ `w r`	**2.** _____	**3.** _____
4. _____	**5.** _____	**6.** _____
7. _____	**8.** _____	**9.** _____

 Helping at Home Tell your child that you are going to read words that begin with the letter *w*. Some words will have silent *w*. Have your child clap if he or she cannot hear the sound of *w* in the word: *wrench, wag, write, wring, wave, windmill, wing, wish, wrinkle, wrong.*

McGraw-Hill School Division

ONE WRITER'S

DIARY

by Janet Craig
photos by Amy and Richard Hutchings

May 5

Dear Diary,

I am almost out of space and I haven't even decided what to write.

I know! I'll write a book called "How to Write a Book!" And this is it! My book is finished. It is very simple to write a book.

the end!

by Lucy

Helping at Home Your child has read this book in school. Have him or her read it aloud to you. Then have your child write a diary entry about something he or she did at school.

Dear Diary,

May 1

I am going to write a book!

If I follow some simple rules, maybe words will go from my brain to my wrist to my pen—and, at last, to the paper.

I am going to share my writing secrets only with you.

When will I begin to write?

Tomorrow!

Your friend, the writer,

Lucy

McGraw-Hill School Division

Now I am tired, Dear Diary. And that is the wrong way to write a book! No one ever wrote a good book when she was tired.

What to do? Head to the tub for a bath. Until tomorrow—

Your friend, the writer,

Lucy

May 2

Dear Diary,

Before I write, I must decide what to write about.

I will write a list of subjects and characters. Here is my list:

Making a Parachute

My Trip to Chicago

Chef Paul's Cooking Secrets

The Laugh Book

Which one do I choose? I'll have to take a walk and think about that.

Your friend, the writer,

Lucy

May 4

Dear Diary,

What a day! The sun is shining.

The birds are singing together like a chorus. But it is wrong to think I can start writing.

Before starting to write, a writer must relax.

I think I'll do some warm-ups.

1. Do ten jumping jacks.

2. Jog in place.

3. Wriggle my fingers.

4. Shake my wrists.

May 3

Dear Diary,

At last the day is here! It's the day I begin to write my book. But first I must get ready. Here is what I need to do:

1. Find a pen. I think I left mine in school. I'll use a pencil.

2. Find paper. I take the wrapper off a pad of nice white paper. I stare at all the smooth sheets.

McGraw-Hill School Division

3. Find a desk to write on. Mine wobbles and I have to fix it. I'll fold up this wrapper and put it under the leg.

At last, all is ready. But am I? No. My head aches and I am so tired! I have to take a nap.

Your friend, the writer,

Lucy

ch

Name _____

Choose the word that completes the sentence.
Write the word.

chef mechanic orchestra machine parachute

I. The washing machine is broken.

2. The _____ made a yummy sauce.

3. The _____ will fix the car.

4. Chris plays drums in the _____ .

5. The _____ catches the wind.

 Helping at Home To help your child practice reading words with the *ch* sound as in *Chicago* or in *school*, play charades! Write the following words on slips of paper: *orchestra, mechanic, parachute, chef, machine*. Invite your child to choose a slip and pantomime actions so others may guess the word.

silent w

Name _____

Choose the word that completes the sentence. Write the word.

| wrapping wrench wrong wrings write |

I. Bob _____wrings_____ out the mop.

2. Sam took the _____ lunch to school.

3. Mike is good at _____ gifts.

4. Pam likes to _____ letters.

5. She uses a _____ .

Helping at Home Write these words with silent *w* and have your child read them aloud: *wren, write, wrap, wring, wreck*. Have your child write the words and use a red crayon to underline the silent *w*.

Name _____

Fill in the circle in front of the word that names each picture. Write the word.

I. ● school ○ shawl

school

2. ○ nephew ○ dolphin

_____

3. ○ chef ○ clue

_____

4. ○ chrome ○ crawl

_____

5. ○ elephant ○ excited

_____

6. ○ choice ○ chorus

_____

7. ○ chute ○ cute

_____

8. ○ fawn ○ photo

_____

9. ○ pause ○ sauce

_____

Helping at Home To review many of the new words he or she is learning, suggest that your child make a chart of the family's schedule. Have him or her write *schedule* at the top of the chart. Encourage him or her to show all the activities in which family members participate.

Name_____

Circle the missing letters. Then write them.
Read the word.

1.

(wr)
tr

_____
w̲r̲ en

2.

ch
th

_____
_____ ef

3.

au
ai

_____
s _____ cer

4.

ch
wh

_____
s _____ ool

5.

ea
aw

_____
l _____ n

6.

wh
wr

_____
_____ ite

🏠 **Helping at Home** Your child has been learning to read and write words that may be difficult to sound out. Look through magazines with your child and see how many of these words you can find. Make a collage of the words. Possible examples: *write, wrong, photo, telephone, laugh.*

silent k

knot	knob	knee	kneel	knit
knitted	know	known	knew	knock
knife	knead	knuckle	knight	knapsack

Name _____

Write **kn**. Color each picture whose name begins with **kn** as in **knock**.

kn**ock**

‾‾

kn‾‾‾‾‾‾‾‾   ‾‾‾‾‾‾‾‾   ‾‾‾‾‾‾‾‾   ‾‾‾‾‾‾‾‾

McGraw-Hill School Division

 Helping at Home To practice silent *k* words, play a Simon Says game in which you ask your child to slap his or her knees, kneel on one knee, rap his or her knuckles on a tabletop, and knock on a door. Emphasize the words *knee, kneel, knuckles,* and *knock,* all of which contain a silent *k*.

The Farmer Who Knew Birds

by Betsy Franco

illustrated by Kathleen Kuchera

Many weeks passed. One day, there was a knocking sound. The farmer turned the knob and looked outside.

He saw four giant eagles! One had the knitted blanket in his beak.

"We came to thank you," said the mother eagle. "If you ever need help, wave this blanket and we will come."

Then the four giant eagles flew back to the cliffs.

 Helping at Home Your child has read this book in school. Read it together at home. Then have him or her read it aloud and write the words that contain a silent *k*.

8

Once there was a giant eagle who had three giant eggs. The mother eagle knew she needed help keeping them warm.

One day, she saw a farmer kneeling down to feed some birds.

"He can sit on my eggs!" she said.

"I do not mind, Mother Eagle," he said.

"I know you need me."

So the eagle picked up the farmer and flew him to her nest up in the cliffs.

For three days, the girl knit a giant blanket and tied it with a knot.

All three girls put on their boots. They put food and water in their knapsacks.

They took the knitted blanket up the hill.

At the eagle's nest, they kneeled down. They wrapped the knitted blanket around the mother eagle's eggs.

"You can come home now, father," they said.

McGraw-Hill School Division

2

7

The farmer's three girls saw him fly away. "How can we get father back?" they asked each other.

"I know what to do," said the first girl. She made a giant oat cake for the eagle. She started up the hill, but soon she was very tired. She stumbled and fell to her knees. The cake flew up.

"If only I had known how steep it is!" the girl said. She turned around and went back home.

At the top of the hill, the girl saw her father sitting on the eagle eggs. "Why are you here, father?" she asked.

"My girl," said her father, "I am keeping the eggs warm, but I am getting a bit tired."

"I know just what to do, father," said the girl. "I will be back soon."

The middle girl said, "I know what to do. I will go when the eagle is sleeping. Then I will bring father home."

She put food and water in a knapsack and started out. But part way up the hill, she tripped on a rock. She hurt her knees and skinned her knuckles.

"If only I had known how rocky it is!" she cried. She turned around and went back home.

McGraw-Hill School Division

The third girl said, "I do not know what to do. But I will try to find out."

She put food and water in a knapsack. She tied it with a strong knot. Then she started out.

Up the hill she climbed, with her knapsack on her back.

Name _____

Circle the word that names each picture.

1.

knee ~~(knuckle)~~

2.

knob   now

3.

puppy   kitten

4.

knock   knack

5.

kneel   kick

6.

knife   nice

7.

kite   knit

8.

net   knit

9.

knot   know

 Helping at Home Dictate silent *k* words and have your child use markers to write them in large letters on a grocery bag: *knapsack, knuckle, knock, knew, knit, knot, know.* Cut long strips from another grocery bag and securely attach them to the top and the bottom of the bag to create a "Silent *k*" knapsack.

Practicing silent *k*   217

Name_____

Circle the word that names each picture.
Write the word.

1. 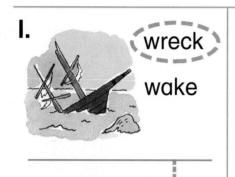 (wreck) wake	**2.**  anger anchor	**3.** 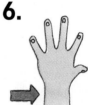 knit kitten
wreck		
4.  knife kite	**5.** phone photo	**6.**  wrist waist
7.  blew beauty	**8.**  range wrench	**9.**  knock write

Helping at Home Your child has learned many new words. For practice, encourage your child to write a story or poem using as many of these words as he or she can: *beauty, school, chorus, ruler, royalty, photograph, writer, knit.*

silent b

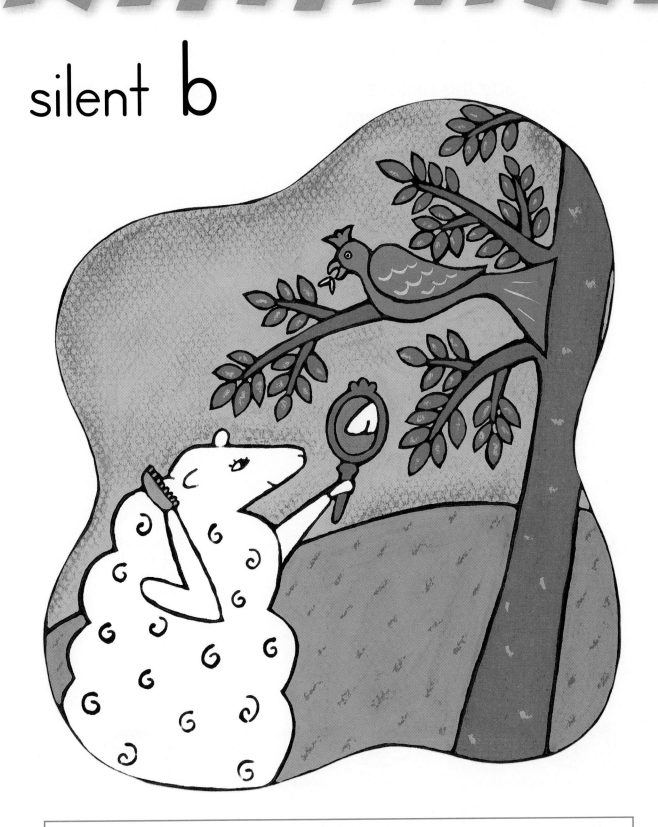

| lamb | comb | limb | numb | dumb |
| thumb | crumb | plumber | climb | doubt |

silent b

Name_____

Say the picture name. Circle the words with a silent **b** as in **lamb**.

lamb

1.  (climb)	**2.**  comb	**3.** web
4.  limb	**5.**  beets	**6.**  bib
7. thumb	**8.**  crumbs	**9.** brown

 Helping at Home To familiarize your child with words in which the letter *b* is silent, say these phrases and have your child respond with a word that has a silent *b*: four fingers and a ____ (*thumb*); hairbrush and ____ (*comb*); a mother sheep and her ____ (*lamb*), trees with large ____ (*limbs*).

McGraw-Hill School Division

silent l

talk	talking	walk	walking	half
calf	calm	palm	stalk	chalk
folks	could	would	should	sidewalk

silent l

Name _____

The letter **l** can be silent as in the word **yolk**. Read each word. Circle the picture that the word names.

yolk

1.

chalk

2.

calf

3.

palm

4.

half

 Helping at Home To practice silent *l*, say these words and ask your child to respond with rhyming words: *walk (talk, chalk, stalk), calm (palm, balm), calf (half), should (could, would)*. Write each word mentioned by your child. Have him or her read the words and underline each silent letter.

Introducing silent *l*

Calm Sally

by Jennifer Jacobson

illustrated by Suzette Barbier

. . . trade the palm tree for some lemonade?"

"Yes!" I said. "Yes, Yes, Yes!"

Funny things can happen.

Helping at Home Your child has read this book in school. Take turns reading it aloud. Then have your child tell about the funny things that happened to Sally.

8

Funny things can happen. One day I sold lemonade. A farmer and his calf and lamb came walking down the road. The farmer wanted lemonade.

"That will be ten cents," I said.

"I don't have ten cents," said the farmer. "But you can have my calf and my lamb."

The farmer handed me the rope and walked off.

I had not made one cent yet.

"Stay calm, Sally," I said to myself. "You know what to do."

I took my chalk and wrote:
PALM TREE FOR SALE $5

Before long, someone came walking down the road. "Ooo, doesn't that tree look nice!" she said. "I must have that palm tree. I doubt that I have the money," she said, "but would you, could you . . .

Name_____

Circle the word that names each picture.

1.

came (crumbs)

2.

awning dawn

3.

lamb lamp

4.

alphabet after

5.

palm park

6.

needle knee

7.

yawn yolk

8.

comb dome

9.

rent wren

 Helping at Home Have your child draw a large thumb and play "Thumb-Up-Thumb-Down."
Spell the following words, some correctly; some not: *knot, talk, comb, wrist, could, glue, pour*. Have
your child point "thumb up" when you spell the word correctly and "thumb down" when you don't.

Name_____

Read each word. Circle the picture that the word names. Then circle the silent letter in the word.

1. climb	
2. knee	
3. wrist	
4. talk	
5. thumb	

 Helping at Home Write each of these words on two separate cards: *knob, comb, chalk, walk, plumber, wrist, write, wrong, knock, calf.* Mix the cards and turn them face down. Turn over two cards and read them. If the words match, keep the cards. If not, turn them face down. Take turns.

silent
g
h
gh

gnat	gnaw	gnome	gnarled	
oh	hour	honor	honest	exhibit
right	night	might	sight	light
fight	flight	bright	sigh	high
thigh	straight	caught	taught	daughter
tight	daylight	moonlight	mighty	

silent g h gh	Name _____

Say the picture name.
Circle the words with silent **g**, **h**, or **gh**.

 night    gnaw    hour

1. (gnat)	**2.**  right	**3.**  goose
4.  herbs	**5.**  house	**6.**  high
7.  flight	**8.**  sign	**9.**  girl

 Helping at Home To practice words with silent letters, write these words on cards and place them face down on the tabletop: *oh, gnat, gnaw, sign, flight, night, herb, honor, honest, sight, right.* Have your child select a card, read the word, and place it in either a silent *g*, silent *h*, or silent *gh* pile.

232   Introducing silent *g*, silent *h*, silent *gh*

NIGHT BIRDS

by Robert Newell

illustrated by Drew-Brook-Cormack Assoc.

Would you like to see an owl? You might! Honest! Owls live where there are tall trees or high ledges.

Watch for gray, furry pellets on the ground. If you see some, look straight up. Look high.

Don't forget that owls hide in the daylight hours. Take your time. Look hard. You might see bright, shiny owl eyes looking back at you!

 Helping at Home Your child has read this book in school. Have him or her read it aloud to you. Then have your child write the story words that have silent *g, h,* or *gh.*

8

It is a ghostly, cold winter night. A bright blanket of snow shines in the moonlight.

"Hoo–hoo. Hoo–hoo–hoot."

It's an owl! Do you see him? There he is. Right there, high up in that pine tree. Oh! What a beautiful sight!

An owl can eat a mouse in a few mighty gulps. A small barn owl eats about three mice each night. That's over 1,000 mice a year!

A few hours after they eat, owls spit up a gray pellet. A pellet is a sign that an owl lives nearby.

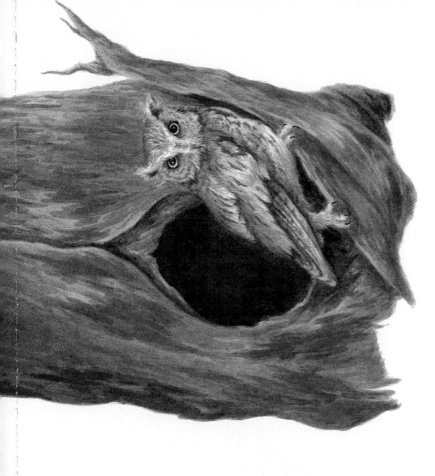

Owls hoot and screech on winter nights. They are calling to each other. Soon they will find nests and lay eggs. They might settle in a hollow tree, in a hawk's nest, or in a high nook in a barn. Some even nest right on the ground.

This is a screech owl. He looks like a little brown gnome. He is the same color as the tree trunk. If he sits tight, no one will see him.

Oh, an owl's ears are amazing, too! High on its perch, an owl can hear the slightest scratching under the snow and leaves below.

Other birds make noise when they fly. Not owls! Their wings make a sound like the softest of sighs. This long-eared owl has caught a mouse.

Owl eggs hatch in late winter, around March. In daylight, all the owls doze for hours. But when night is near, owls take flight to hunt.

Owls gnaw on lots of things, such as mice, snakes, frogs, rabbits, even skunks.

Owlets are always hungry. It will take a lot of food to feed these little owls. Their parents must be exhausted from all that hunting!

McGraw-Hill School Division

Did you ever notice that owls seem to stare straight at you? That's because owls' eyes can't look left and right. But owls can turn their necks right around so they can see behind them.

An owl's sight is amazing. Its eyes have shiny walls inside, so it can see well in very dim light. To see, a little moonlight is all this barn owl needs!

silent g h gh

Name _____

Choose the word that completes the sentence. Write the word.

bright	high	hour	sign	straight

1.

Use a ruler to draw a  **straight** line.

2.

The sun is _____ today.

3.

A plane can fly _____ in the sky.

4.

We snack at the _____ of 12 noon.

5.

This _____ tells cars to stop.

 Helping at Home To practice words that contain silent letters, print these phrases for your child to read aloud: *exhausted knight, bright light, high flight, exhibit sign*. Then ask your child to write sentences with each phrase and use a bright crayon to underline the silent letters.

Name_____

Fill in the circle in front of the word that names
each picture.

1.

⬤ sign   ○ sidewalk

2.

○ light   ○ flight

3.

○ calf   ○ half

4.

○ lamb   ○ lab

5.

○ sauce   ○ saw

6.

○ knee   ○ knot

7.

○ chalk   ○ check

8.

○ laugh   ○ limb

9.

○ wrap   ○ write

McGraw-Hill School Division

ea

head	read	dead	lead	bread
thread	dread	ready	steady	already
spread	deaf	health	healthy	wealthy
meant	feather	leather	weather	heavy
sweat	breath	meadow	pleasant	instead
great	steak	break	daybreak	

ea

Great has the long **a** sound. **Bread** has the short **e** sound. Read each word. Circle the picture that the word names.

great

bread

1.

head

2.

break

3.

steak

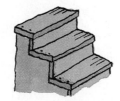 

4.

thread

 Helping at Home Print these words on cards: *great, steak, break, daybreak, head, bread, measure.* Make up a sentence for each of the words, saying "blank" instead of the word. Have your child complete the sentence with the best word.

ea

Name_____

Circle the word that completes the sentence. Write the word.

1.

My jacket is made of _leather_ .

feather

(leather)

light

2.

The bag of fruit is _____ .

healthy

heavy

honest

3.

Nan eats toast at _____ .

daybreak

steak

instead

4.

Breakfast looks _____ .

grapes

weather

great

5.

It is hard to _____ a needle.

thread

three

break

Helping at Home Your child is learning words with the short *e* and long *a* sounds of *ea*. Write the following words on separate cards: *steak, heavy, sweater, break, head, great, weather*. Hold up each card and ask your child to say the word and to clap once if he or she hears short *e* and twice for long *a*.

ea

Circle the word that names each picture.

Name_____

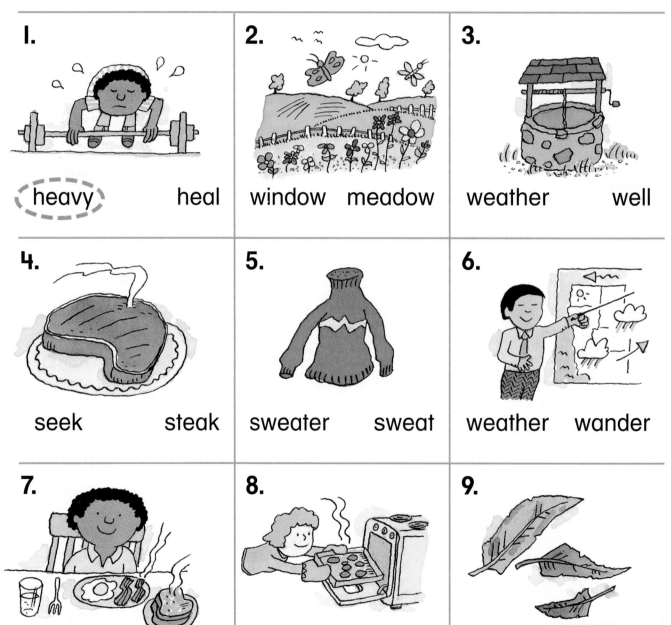

1. ~~heavy~~ heal

2. window   meadow

3. weather   well

4. seek   steak

5. sweater   sweat

6. weather   wander

7. breakfast   read

8. break   bake

9. feathers   health

Helping at Home Your child is learning to read words that have the short *e* and long *a* sounds of *ea*. Practice by taking turns pointing out such words the next time you are reading together. Examples: *head, bread, spread, healthy, leather, great, steak, daybreak, breath, read, thread, wealthy*.

242   Introducing /e/*ea*, /ā/*ea*

McGraw-Hill School Division

Cowboy Slim

by Leya Roberts
illustrated by Don Tate

"Great!" said Slim. "Then I am a cowboy!"
He cocked his leather hat and clicked
his leather boots. Cowboy Slim led the
cows from the meadow to the barn.
Then he ran into the house to tell his
mom the news.

 Helping at Home Your child has read this book
in school. Read the story together, with your child saying
the words that Slim says.

8

It was daybreak at the ranch.

"This is a big day," said Slim. "I must get ready."

He put on pants and a shirt. Then he put on leather boots and a leather hat.

"You need to live on a ranch," began the older cow.

"I do that already!" said Slim.

"You need to wear leather boots and a leather hat," said the cow.

"I do that already!" said Slim.

"You have to help us cows get from the meadow to the barn," said Slim.

"I do that, too!" said Slim.

"Well, then you're already a cowboy!" said the cow.

Slim sat down for breakfast. His mom had fixed him steak and eggs.

"I'm going to become a cowboy today," Slim said to his mom as he ate.

"Oh?" said his mom.

"I'm already a boy. I need to find out how to be a cow," he added. He got up to go.

"Wait," said his mom. But Slim was already on his way out the door.

An older cow was standing by.

"Come on!" she said to the first cow. "You don't need to act like a cow to be a cowboy!"

"I don't?" asked Slim.

"He doesn't?" asked the young cow.

"Then what do I need to do?" asked Slim.

Slim led his horse out of the barn and rode into the meadow. The cows were already in the field.

"What a pleasant day to become a cowboy," said Slim. He rode up to the cows.

Slim went up to a young cow and took a deep breath.

"I want to be a cowboy. I'm already a boy. Can you tell me how to be a cow?" he asked.

McGraw-Hill School Division

"Well, here's what I do," said the cow. "I stand in the meadow and say MOOO."

"I can do that," said Slim.

"When I need a break, I lie in the shade," said the cow.

"I can do that," said Slim.

"And," said the cow, "I eat grass for breakfast, lunch, and dinner."

"That doesn't sound very pleasant," said Slim. "But I'll do it!"

ea

Name _____

Choose the word that completes the sentence. Write the word.

| steak | healthy | break | instead | great |

1. He would rather bike ⸺instead⸺ .

2. Cook the _____ on a grill.

3. She is a _____ horse rider.

4. An apple is a _____ snack.

5. He will _____ the batting record.

 Helping at Home Fold a paper in half the long way. At the top of the left side write *ea* long *a*. On the right side write *ea* short *e*. Read words such as the following and have your child list them under the proper heading. Examples: *great, health, break, head, breakfast, daybreak, pleasant.*

Name _____

Circle the missing letters. Then write them.
Read the word.

1.

wr

(kn)

k̲n̲ead

2.

gh

ph

cau____t

3.

ee

ea

thr____d

4.

b

l

ha____f

5.

b

p

lam____

6.

ir

ea

st____k

McGraw-Hill School Division

ear

earn	early	earth	heard	pearl
learn	learning	search	searching	
bear	pear	wear	tear	
heart	hearth			

ear

Name _____

Circle the sentence that tells about the picture.

early   bear   heart

1.

(Seth is learning to add.)

Seth is learning to read.

2.

The earth spins around the sun.

The moon spins around the stars.

3.

I heard my brother cry.

I heard my puppy cry.

4.

There is a pear in my lunchbox.

There is an apple in my lunchbox.

5.

I earn money for washing the dishes.

I earn money for washing the car.

Helping at Home To help your child read words with the different sounds *ear* makes, encourage her or him to point out such words in books and comic strips, menus, street signs, and advertisements. Examples: *earn, early, earth, pearl, bear, wear, tear, heart.*

Introducing *ear*

The Pearl of Knowledge

by **Tom Fen**
illustrated by **Robin DeWitt**

Mouse went back to his home under the pear tree. He soon fell asleep.

As he slept, the moon rose in the sky. Moonlight shone on Mouse, and he smiled.

In his dream, Mouse saw the pearl of knowledge and felt like the wisest one on Earth.

Helping at Home Your child has read this book in school. Have him or her read it aloud to you. Then have your child pretend to be the mouse, and tell about his adventures.

8

Mouse lived in a house under a pear tree. One night he looked out and saw a round, white thing stuck in the top of the pear tree.

"That must be the pearl of knowledge," said sleepy Mouse. "I have seen it in my dreams. If I can get it, I will be the wisest one on Earth."

"I can't climb the pear tree now," he said. "I will get the pearl of knowledge in the morning."

Mouse was so sad he started to cry.

"Stop, stop," said Bird. "It breaks my heart to hear you cry. I will help you."

Mouse stopped crying and told Bird the whole story.

"That is easy," said Bird. "Go home to your pear tree. Get into bed. Look out your window. There you will find the pearl of knowledge."

Mouse got up early the next morning, but there was nothing in the pear tree.

"The pearl is gone," he said. "I will search for it and learn where it went. I will find it. Then I will be the wisest one on Earth."

So Mouse set off. His heart was light. He whistled a tune as he went to search for the pearl.

So Mouse went on alone with a heavy heart. Soon he met Bird.

"I am searching for the pearl of knowledge," said Mouse.

"I have flown all over the Earth and I have never heard of it," said Bird.

"The one with the pearl of knowledge will be the wisest one on Earth," said Mouse. "Will you help me search?"

"I already know a lot," said Bird. "I don't need to be wiser."

Soon Mouse met Fox.

"I am searching for the pearl of knowledge," said Mouse. "It was stuck in my pear tree last night."

"I have run all over the Earth and I have never heard of it," said Fox.

"The one with the pearl of knowledge will be the wisest one on Earth," said Mouse. "Will you help me search?"

"I am the quickest on Earth. I don't need to be the wisest," said Fox.

McGraw-Hill School Division

Soon Mouse met Bear.

"I am searching for the pearl of knowledge," said Mouse. "It was stuck in my pear tree last night."

"I have climbed all over the Earth and I have never heard of it," said Bear.

"The one with the pearl of knowledge will be the wisest one on Earth," said Mouse. "Will you help me search?"

"I am the strongest one on Earth. I don't need to be the wisest," said Bear.

ear

Name_____

Choose the word that completes the sentence. Write the word.

| pear | heart | learn | heard | wear |

1. Mom told me what to ___wear___ .

2. The _____ is lacy.

3. This _____ is juicy.

4. Did you _____ to read in school?

5. She _____ the train coming.

 Helping at Home Make two sets of cards for these words: *earn, early, learn, bear, pear, earth, heard, wear, search, pearl, tear, heart.* You and your child should each hold one set. Draw a card from each other's hand and make up a sentence that contains the word.

Name_____

Fill in the circle in front of the word that names
each picture. Write the word.

1.
○ earn
● earth

earth

2.
○ bread
○ breakfast

3.
○ chef
○ shelf

4.
○ sign
○ sight

5.
○ crumb
○ climb

6.
○ heart
○ heat

7.
○ meadow
○ mellow

8.
○ lamb
○ lame

9.
○ chemist
○ mechanic

McGraw-Hill School Division

ie
ei

chief	thief	brief	grief	belief
relief	shriek	shield	field	yield
piece	niece	grieve	relieve	believe
achieve	berries	ladies	pennies	puppies
ceiling	receive	received	either	neither

Name_____

Write **ie**. Color each picture whose name has the long **e** sound as in **chief**.

chief

_____

i̇e

 Helping at Home To practice words with the long *e* sound of *ie*, play a riddle game. Say for example, "I am thinking of a word that means a loud scream. It has the long *e* sound of *ie*." *(shriek)* Possible words: *chief, field, berries, ladies, piece, pennies, shield, niece, puppies, handkerchief.*

McGraw-Hill School Division

ei

Name_____

Circle the sentence that tells about the picture.

neither

1.  (I expect to receive a party invitation.)

It looks like we have no mail today.

2.  I will wear either a dress or a skirt.

I will wear either a T-shirt or a sweater.

3.  Party decorations hung from the the ceiling.

Party decorations fell to the floor.

4.  Neither the birthday boy nor his mom were there.

Neither the table nor the chair was in the room.

5.  The birthday boy received a big surprise.

The birthday boy fell asleep.

 Helping at Home Your child has been learning that *ei* can have the long *e* sound. Make a list of words with *ei*, long *e* in them and have your child use each one in a sentence. Possible words: *either, conceited, receive, neither.*

ie
ei

Name_____

Choose the word that completes
the sentence. Write the word.

| ceiling either piece shield berries |

1.

The knight has a ___shield___ .

2.

The bowl is full of _____ .

3.

The _____ is cracked.

4.

She does not want _____ of them.

5.

I ate a _____ of apple pie.

 Helping at Home To practice words with the long *e* sound of *ei* and *ie*, play the "I spy" game.
Point to objects whose names contain the long *e* sound of *ei* and *ie*. For example, "I spy some small
round things on the counter." (pennies) Possible words: *ceiling, receipt, puzzle pieces, field.*

McGraw-Hill School Division

LADY'S PUPPIES

by Kathy Mormile
illustrated by Linda Weller

Meg will be very sad when all the puppies are gone. But her mom and dad say she can keep one. That's a relief.

Meg chooses the puppy that was born last.

Meg is excited about her choice. She can't wait until this beautiful puppy grows up — and has puppies of its own.

 Helping at Home Your child has read this book in school. Have him or her read it aloud to you. Then have your child tell how Lady cares for her puppies.

8

Meg is very excited. Her big brown dog, Lady, is going to have puppies.

Meg wants to help her father fix up a place for Lady to have her puppies. The place for Lady to have her puppies. The place must be soft and warm. Meg's father says that torn paper will be soft. But Meg adds a piece of her old baby blanket to make the bed a little softer.

Soon the puppies will not need Lady to care for them anymore. They will be ready to go to new homes. Meg can hardly believe she will have the pups for such a brief time.

Meg's dad puts an ad in the newspaper. Meg's family receives many calls from people who want the puppies.

That night, Meg wakes up to the sounds of yipping. She runs downstairs. What a relief! Lady is okay. She's lying on the bed.

Meg knows this is the moment she's been waiting for.

It is hard to believe, but soon Lady has nine healthy puppies. What an achievement!

Growing puppies have plenty of time to play. Meg plays with Lady's puppies in a field in back of the house. Sometimes she brings a soft toy animal or a piece of leather which the puppies love to bite.

4

Lady's chief job now is to take care of her puppies. She feeds them and licks them to keep them clean. She does not like anyone to touch them right now. When puppies are first born, they can neither see nor hear. New puppies can't walk, either.

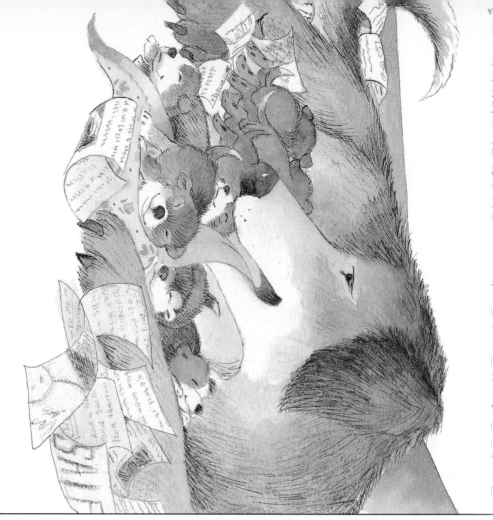

Puppies are helpless for only a brief time. They grow much faster than human babies.

When puppies are two weeks old, they can see. When they are four weeks old, they begin to walk around. They are very nosy.

5

ie
ei

Name_____

Circle the word that completes the sentence.
Write the word.

1.

Ted left five _pennies_ on the table.

(pennies)
beliefs
pinches

2.

Jan likes _____ peanut butter nor jelly.

either
neither
bright

3.

I want _____ soup or a sandwich.

either
ceiling
nor

4.

The farmer works in the _____ .

field
fight
found

5.

Hooray! This puzzle _____ fits.

piece
place
shield

Helping at Home To practice the long *e* sound of both *ei* and *ie*, make cards for words that
contain both letter combinations. Ask your child to read the word cards and put them into separate
piles. Possible words: *ceiling, conceit, chief, relief, achieve, deceit, yield, shield, perceive, field.*

Name_____

Circle the word that names each picture.

1.

peer   (pear)

2.

pennies   puppies

3.

light   like

4.

ceiling   seal

5.

pears   pearls

6.

teacher   sweater

7.

pace   piece

8.

wrap   ramp

9.

palm   pond

McGraw-Hill School Division

 Helping at Home To help your child practice new words, ask him or her to write a story about what happens to a farmer as he or she works in a field. Possible words: *play, pear, berries, earth, search, spread, treasure, gnat, herbs.*

ei
eigh
ey

vein	reins	reindeer	veil
sleigh	weigh	neigh	neighbor
weight	freight	eight	eighteen
they	prey	obey	

ei
eigh
ey

Name_____

Veil, neigh, and **they** have the long **a** sound. Read each word. Circle the picture that the word names.

neigh   veil   they

I. eight	
2. sleigh	
3. reins	 
4. obey	

 Helping at Home To practice the long *a* sound of *ey, ei,* and *eigh,* have your child read and write the following words: *obey, they, reindeer, eight, neigh, survey, weigh, vein.*

ei
eigh
ey

Name _____

Circle the word that completes the sentence.
Write the word.

1.

We must _____obey_____ the rules.

obey
prey
whey

2.

Look at the _____ in this leaf.

veins
veils
weigh

3.

The big fish chases its _____ .

obey
prey
they

4.

I am _____ years old today.

eight
eighteen
ten

5.

We ride in a _____ each winter.

weigh
freight
sleigh

Helping at Home To practice the long *a* sound of *ei, eigh,* and *ey*, play a riddle game.
Say, for example, "I'm thinking of a sound that horses make. Its name has *eigh*. What is it?" *(neigh)*
Possible words: *eight, veil, vein, reins, reindeer, eighteen, neighbor, sleigh, weigh, weight, prey, obey.*

ei
eigh
ey

Name_____

Circle the sentence that tells about the picture.

 veil

 neigh

 they

1.

(Pull back on the reins to stop the horse.)

The boy and the horse jump the fence.

2.

Jennifer weighs 69 pounds.

The doctor weighs 69 pounds.

3.

Matt is driving a sleigh.

Matt is eighteen years old.

4.

Our neighbors are coming for dinner.

Our neighbors are moving away.

5.

They are neighbors.

They are twins.

 Helping at Home To practice words with the long *a* sound as in *reindeer, sleigh,* and *they,* write the following on paper: *eight, neighbor, obey, reins, sleigh, veil.* Ask your child to use as many of these long *a* words as he or she can in a picture of a wintry night.

Introducing /ā/ *ei, eigh, ey*

The New Neighbors

by Allan M. Cornell

illustrated by Roz Schanzer

"That was so great!" said James.

"The reindeer are wonderful neighbors," said his mom.

"And I hear," said his dad, "that we have new neighbors on the other side of our house, too."

"Yes," said Mindy. "But they can't be half as much fun as the reindeer!"

"You're right!" said James.

 Helping at Home Have your child read this book aloud to you. Then have him or her tell what would be fun about having neighbors who are talking reindeer.

8

Something was very strange! James ran to get a better look. He counted eight woolly shapes. Were these the new neighbors? James walked closer.

"You're not sheep. You're not cows," whispered James. "Hey!" he shouted.

"You're all reindeer!"

"I know that," said one of the reindeer.

"You're a *talking* reindeer!" said James.

"I'm Stella," said the talking reindeer.

McGraw-Hill School Division

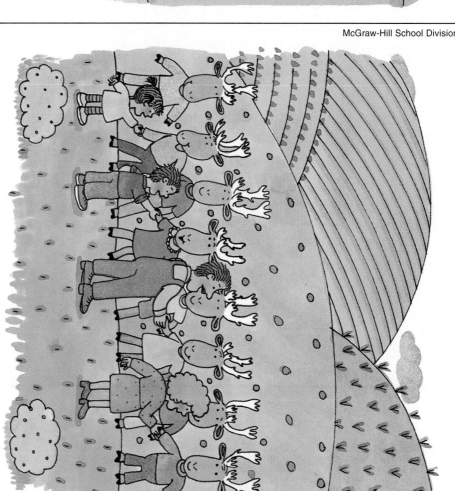

"Thank you so much!" James and his family said to their new neighbors. "You will have to come to our house soon—all eight of you."

"We would like that," said Stella. "Just give us a call."

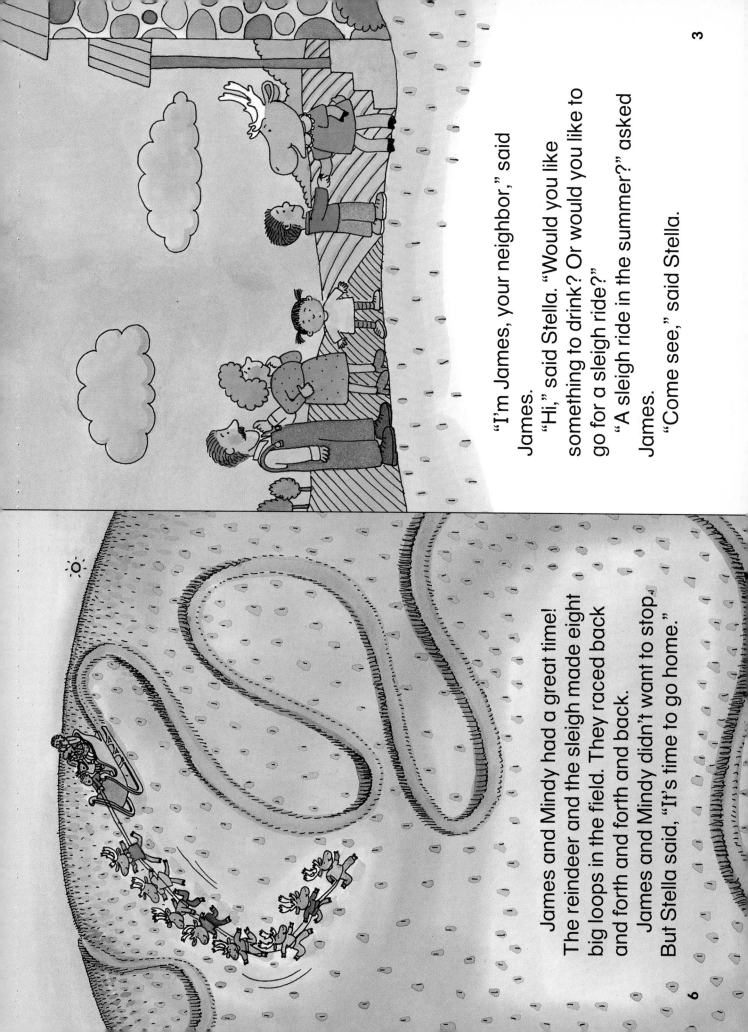

"I'm James, your neighbor," said James.

"Hi," said Stella. "Would you like something to drink? Or would you like to go for a sleigh ride?"

"A sleigh ride in the summer?" asked James.

"Come see," said Stella.

James and Mindy had a great time! The reindeer and the sleigh made eight big loops in the field. They raced back and forth and forth and back.

James and Mindy didn't want to stop. But Stella said, "It's time to go home."

Stella showed the sleigh to James, his mom, dad, and sister, Mindy. Then she handed James the reins to the sleigh.

"Hold onto the reins tightly. We weigh a lot. Eight reindeer can feel like eighteen reindeer when we pull the sleigh fast."

"Anything you say," said James.

Stella neighed and said, "Put on your seat belts. Let's go!"

McGraw-Hill School Division

The reindeer raced down the field.

"Pull the reins to the left," ordered Stella. James obeyed. The eight reindeer turned left.

"Pull the reins to the right," said Stella. James obeyed. The eight reindeer turned right. All of those reindeer running together should have sounded like a freight train. But they were as quiet as butterflies.

ei
eigh
ey

Name _____

Choose the word that completes the sentence.
Write the word.

| they | eight | obey | veil | weigh |

1.
Her hat has a _____ veil _____ .

2.
She knocked down _____ pins.

3.
What are _____ hiding?

4.
I taught my dog to _____ .

5.
How much do you _____ ?

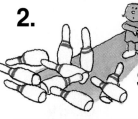 **Helping at Home** To practice words with the long *a* sound of *ey*, *ei*, and *eigh*, say the following
words. Have your child give "thumbs up" if the word has the sound of long *a* and "thumbs down" if
not. Possible words: *hey, heart, pear, vein, neighbor, they, hour, eighteen, whey, would, obey, thumb.*

Name _____

Fill in the circle in the front of the word that
names each picture. Write the word.

1.
○ night
● weigh

weigh

2.
○ daughter
○ dotted

3.
○ veins
○ breaks

4.
○ leather
○ letter

5.
○ pennies
○ puppies

6.
○ today
○ obey

7.
○ nest
○ neigh

8.
○ early
○ pearls

9.
○ reins
○ royal

 Helping at Home Encourage your child to show off his or her reading skills. Take turns reading
street signs, posters, books, advertisements, comic strips, and so on. Ask him or her to come up with
rhyming words for those words that he or she reads.

McGraw-Hill School Division

ough

tough	rough	enough	
dough	though	although	doughnut
bought	ought	thought	fought
cough	trough		
through			
bough			

ough

Name_____

Circle the sentence that tells about the picture.

rough   cough   dough

1.

(Linda used rough sandpaper.)

Linda fixed the table with glue.

2.

He is eating doughnuts.

He is in bed with a cough.

3.

It rained although the sun was shining.

It rained on the cruise ship.

4.

This horse drinks from a lake.

This horse drinks from a trough.

5.

He had enough pennies to make a dime.

He didn't have enough pennies to make a dime.

McGraw-Hill School Division

Helping at Home To practice *ough*, use a rough and smooth surface. Say aloud: *tough, though, although, enough, doughnut.* If the *ough* sounds like *rough*, have your child trace *ough* on a rough surface. If it sounds like *dough*, have your child trace *ough* on a smooth surface.

Introducing *ough*

ough

Name_____

Bough rhymes with **cow**. **Through** rhymes with **too**. **Thought** rhymes with **taught**. Circle and write the word that completes each sentence.

1.

The car goes _through_ the tunnel.

thread
(through)
though

2.

Tim _____ the book was funny.

bought
ought
thought

3.

Lynn _____ a present for her sister.

bought
ought
thought

4.

You _____ to feed your pet fish.

bought
ought
through

5.

The tree _____ bent in the wind.

bough
bought
brought

 Helping at Home Say the following pairs of words and have your child tell you whether or not they rhyme: *bough/now; though/true; rough/tough; brought/throw; bought/thought; ought/taught; caught/night.* Help your child create a rhyming couplet from one of the word pairs.

Name_____

Choose the word that completes the sentence. Write the word.

bought cough doughnut through tough

1.

This math test is  !

2.

A _____ is a sweet treat.

3.

I have a stuffed nose and a _____ .

4.

Put the thread _____ the needle.

5.

I _____ two new pencils for school.

Helping at Home Fasten a small paper plate to a large paper plate at the center. Around the edge of the smaller plate, write *r, t, en, c, tr, d, th, alth, b, thr.* At the edge of the large plate, write *ough.* Turn the larger plate so the letters align to form words. Have your child read the words.

Enough

by Anne W. Phillips

illustrated by Robin Rorabach

The baker's daughter handed the old
lady all the loaves.

"Is this enough?" she asked. "More
than enough," said the old lady. "Thanks."

After that, the baker's daughter always
gave big loaves of bread to people. It
made her happy to think she was being
as kind as she ought to be. It also made
her father proud of her.

And that was enough, after all.

 Helping at Home Your child has read this book in
school. Help him or her read it aloud. Then ask your child
why the girl was happy when she learned to be generous.

8

Once there was a baker who had a daughter. She helped him mix the dough, make the bread, and sell the loaves that his neighbors bought.

Although the baker was kind, his daughter was not. Her heart was as small and tough as a week-old crust.

The baker's daughter was a little afraid. She ran to tell her father.

"How did this happen?" she said. "Did the lady trick me?"

The baker thought about it.

"I do not know if she tricked you," he said. "I do know one thing, though. The kinder you are, the happier you will be."

One day an old lady came into the shop. Her dress was ragged. Her hands were rough from hard work.

"It is supper time. Do you have a bit of dough to spare?" the old lady asked.

The baker's daughter did not want to give the old lady anything. But her father had told her she ought to be kind. She pinched off a tiny lump of dough.

"That's enough for her," thought the baker's daughter.

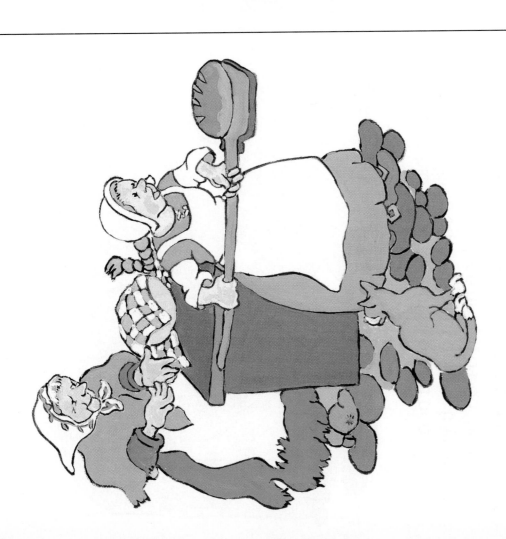

One last time the baker's daughter pinched off a bit of dough. It was smaller than a button.

She put the dough in the oven.

This time when she returned, the loaf of bread was twice as big as the others.

4

"And would you be kind enough to bake it for me?" she asked.

Though the baker's daughter grumbled, she put the scrap of dough in the oven.

The girl went to work in the back room. When she came back, there was a large loaf of bread in the oven.

"Where did that come from?" thought the baker's daughter. "That's more than enough for her."

She hid the large loaf of bread and pinched off a smaller bit of dough. It was only enough to fill the hole in a doughnut.

The baker's daughter put the tiny lump of dough in the oven. Once more she worked out back. Once more a large loaf was in the oven when she returned.

"That's more than enough for her," thought the baker's daughter.

And she hid this large loaf, too.

5

ough

Name _____

Circle the word that completes the sentence. Write the word.

1.

Ben had __enough__ to eat.

although
(enough)
ought

2.

Dad says he _____ to drink milk.

although
bought
ought

3.

_____ Li likes dogs, she owns a cat.

Although
Enough
Ought

4.

She eats cookie _____ out of the bowl.

bough
cough
dough

5.

Mom _____ nuts to mix into the dough.

bough
bought
though

 Helping at Home Ask your child to pretend he or she is guiding you through a tour of a bakery. Have your child use the following words on the tour: *dough, doughnuts, bought, thought, ought, through, although,* and *though.*

ough

Choose the word that completes the sentence.
Write the word.

| trough doughnut rough through though |

1.

The road is ___r o u g h___ and full of holes.

2.

The horse drinks at the _____ .

3.

Ted likes a _____ with his milk.

4.

It's chilly even _____ it's spring.

5.

We went _____ the funhouse tunnel.

 Helping at Home Write the following pairs of rhyming words side by side on cards: *tough/rough,*
cough/trough, rough/enough, bought/thought. Read them together and cut each card in half, separating
the words. Mix the cards and ask your child to put the cards together to match the rhyming words.

Practicing *ough*

Name _____

Circle the missing letters. Then write them.
Read the word.

I.

ea
ie

st __ea__ k

2.

ear
eigh

_____ t

3.

oi
ough

d _____

4.

oo
ough

b _____ t

5.

ea
ee

f _____ ther

6.

ough
ank

t _____

Name_____

Circle the word that names each picture.

1. (rough)　smooth

2. berry　　berries

3. dough　doughnut

4. stew　　through

5. eight　　eighteen

6. shriek　　shield

7. earth　　early

8. twirls　　pearls

9. cough　　trough

Helping at Home Place the following word cards around the room and play a "hunt and seek" game with your child: *bought, through, doughnut, enough, pennies, receive, obey, either, learn, heart, health, steak.* As your child finds each word, have him or her read it aloud and use it in a sentence.

y
ui

gym	gymnast	gymnastics	myth
mystery	symbol	rhythm	physics
physical	physician	typical	crystal
build	building	built	

y
ui

Name_____

Circle the sentence that tells about the picture.

 build

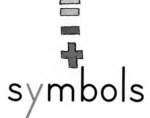 symbols

 mystery

1.

2+2=4

(A plus sign is a symbol that means add.)

A plus sign means take away.

2.

My mother and I are building a fence.

My brother and I are building a tree house.

3.

Max's missing lunch is a mystery.

Max has a peanut butter sandwich for lunch.

4.

Gena plays the rhythm on the drums.

Gena plays sweet sounds on the flute.

5.

We play dodge ball in physical education.

We play checkers in gym class.

 Helping at Home Write these words on cards numbered 1-6: *mystery, building, symbol, physician, typical, myth.* Display the cards. Tell your child you are thinking of a number between 1 and 6; he or she must guess and define the word that matches the number.

Introducing /i/ *y, ui*

McGraw-Hill School Division

Tasha's Dream

by Dona McDuff

•

illustrated by Susan Spellman

It is the day of the Gymnastics Meet.
"The last gymnast is Tasha Guild,"
cries the announcer. "She is in third place
going into this final event."
I mount the beam, moving with a
smooth rhythm through my skills. I finish
with a twisting somersault.

My dream is to win a gold medal. It
didn't happen today. But I won't quit trying
until my dream comes true.

 Helping at Home Your child has read this book in
school. Have him or her read it aloud to you. Then talk
about your child's own dreams for the future.

The crowd cheers as I somersault off the beam and nail the landing.

"The winner of the gold medal in gymnastics is . . . ."

. . . .

"Wake up, Tasha. Time for gymnastics." My mother calls and I leave my dream.

Ever since I was four years old, I have wanted to be a gymnast. My dream is to be a gold-medal gymnast, too.

The last part of our practice is my favorite. I really love the moves we do to music. I listen to the rhythm of the music. I cartwheel quickly to the other side of the mat, adding a headstand roll. The music builds as I build speed.

"Super workout today," Crystal tells us. "See you at the Gymnastics Meet." Crystal waves good-bye.

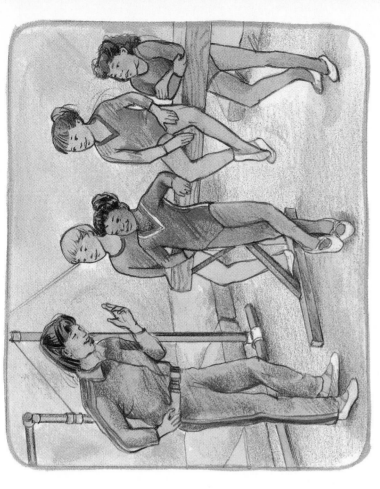

"Let's go, Tasha. The building opens at 9 o'clock," my mother calls again.

I'm going to gymnastics class. Today is the last time to work on our moves before the State Gymnastics Meet. After breakfast, Mom drives me to the gym.

"We have a lot of work to do today," says Crystal, my coach. "But first, do all of you have a note from your physician? You have to be in good physical shape to be part of this team."

We do our hardest physical work on the uneven bars. First we rub our hands with chalk dust to keep from slipping.

It is important to keep a steady rhythm as we move back and forth from the low bar to the high bar. Each skill builds into the next. Hip circles build to a handstand. A handstand builds to a twisting turn. A turn builds to the final skill—a backward somersault.

Crystal leads us in warm-ups. "It's really important to warm up for tough physical work," she says.

Warm-ups are not my favorite part of gymnastics! But we need to do them. We do a typical warm-up. I count in rhythm as I stretch.

Next I do some splits. I finish with some back bends. My body looks like a bridge.

4

McGraw-Hill School Division

Everyone lines up beside the beam to watch Crystal go through the moves. "You make it look so easy," I say. "It's no mystery," she tells us. "It just takes hard work."

"Oops!" I cry as I goof on my first beam skill. I try again. My leg slips. "Don't quit," I tell myself. On the next try, I get it right. I move smoothly through the typical gymnastic skills. Back flip. Straddle split. Round-off.

5

y
ui

Name _____

Circle the word that names each picture.

1.

(physician)   penny

2.

ginger   gymnast

3.

build   typical

4.

LIBRARY

building   bridge

5.

$ ¢ # %

search   symbols

6.

belt   built

7.

goose   guilty

8.

rhythm   rough

9.

The Missing Key

mystery   misty

 Helping at Home With your child, brainstorm a list of words with *y, ui, ough, ei, eigh* and *ey*. Then write the words on cards. Together, build a house of cards. Try not to topple your house as you keep building.

Circle the word that names each picture.
Write the word.

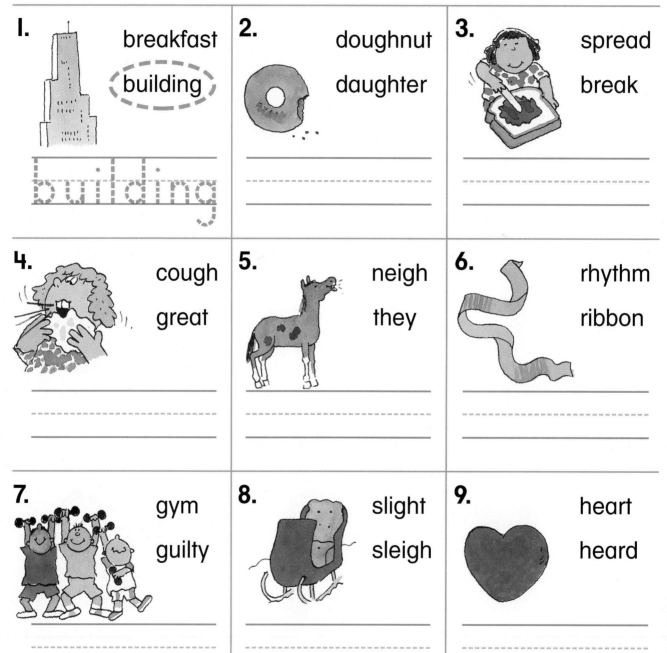

1. breakfast
(building)

building

2. doughnut
daughter

_____

3. spread
break

_____

4. cough
great

_____

5. neigh
they

_____

6. rhythm
ribbon

_____

7. gym
guilty

_____

8. slight
sleigh

_____

9. heart
heard

_____

 Helping at Home Write the following vowel combinations as column heads on a piece of paper: *ui, ough, ei, ie*. Write the following on small pieces of paper: *build, built, thought, brought, veil, reindeer, chief, believe*. Have your child read each word, then put it in the appropriate column.

uy
ui

Guy	buy	buyer	buying
guide	guided	guiding	disguise

Name_____

Circle the sentence that tells about the picture.

buy  disguise

I.

The dog guides the woman across the street.

A man helps the woman cross the street.

2.

The dog nibbles on the flowers.

The dog stops when the woman buys flowers.

3.

The woman is buying daisies.

The woman is buying a tree.

4.

The dog is guiding the woman into the shop.

The dog is guiding the woman out of the shop.

5.

The woman knows the guy in the T-shirt.

The guy in the T-shirt feeds the guide dog.

Helping at Home Have your child start a story using a word of his or her choice from this list of *ui* and *uy* words: *guide, disguise, buy, guy, buying, guiding, guided.* Then you pick a word to continue. Play until all the words have been used. Challenge each other to give the story an ending.

McGraw-Hill School Division

Introducing / ī / *uy, ui*

GUY'S DISGUISE

by Leya Roberts
illustrated by
Chris Demarest

Welcome
to
George Washington
Elementary School

"George Washington's horse, of course," said Guy.

"Well," said Ms. Mason, "I think Guy wins the prize for the best disguise."

Guy couldn't see the blue ribbon that Ms. Mason pinned on him. But he could hear everybody clapping!

 Helping at Home Your child has read this book in school. Have him or her read it aloud. Have your child tell what disguise he or she would wear for History Day.

8

"Don't forget. Tomorrow is History Day," said Ms. Mason. "Everyone will come to school disguised as a famous character from long ago."

"Do you have a costume?" whispered Clyde.

"Not yet," said his friend Guy. "What am I going to do? Everybody will laugh at me if I don't wear a disguise."

"How come they're laughing?" he said. "I'm wearing a disguise just like everyone else."

"Quiet now," said Ms. Mason. "It's time to find out who you're disguised to be."

Soon they had found out what everybody's disguise was . . . except Guy's.

"Come on," said Clyde. "Tell us who you are."

2

7

"Why don't you buy a costume?" said Clyde. "They have some cool ones at that new store on Washington Street. I think it's called Master of Disguise."

"Will you come with me?" asked Guy.

"I'm not good at buying disguises."

"Stick with me," said Clyde. "I'm the best buyer of disguises in town."

At home, Guy tried on the horse costume.

"I can't see!" he cried. "How will I get to school in this disguise?"

"I'll guide you," said Clyde. Clyde guided Guy to school the next day. Guy couldn't see anything. Clyde guided him down the hall and into their classroom. While Clyde was guiding him to his seat, Guy heard a giggle. Then he heard a lot of laughter.

"Hi," said Clyde to the clerk when they got to the disguise store. "This is my pal Guy. He wants to buy a disguise."

"What kind of disguise do you want?" asked the clerk.

Guy didn't say anything. He just pointed.

"What?" said Clyde. "That's a horse costume. What kind of disguise is that?"

"You'll see," said Guy. Then he turned to the clerk and said, "I'll buy that one."

"It might be a little big," said the clerk. But Guy didn't care. He had found the disguise he wanted.

uy
ui

Name_____

Circle the word that completes the sentence.
Write the word.

I. The teacher is _guiding_ the girls.

guide   (guiding)   green

2. Nan is _____ a costume.

buy   buyer   buying

3. Nan likes her clown _____ .

disguise   distant   direction

4. The lighthouse _____ the boat.

guided   guiding   ground

5. Which _____ is the catcher?

buy   buyer   guy

 Helping at Home Your child is learning to recognize words with *ui* and *uy*. Write and read the following with your child: *buy, guy, disguise, guide, guided, guiding*. Take turns using the words in a sentence.

Name_____

Fill in the circle in front of the missing letters.
Then write them. Read the word.

1.

○ ui (filled) ui
○ oi

g __ui__ de

2.

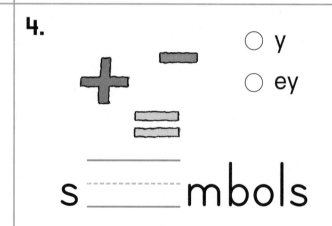

○ ie
○ ui

disg_____se

3.

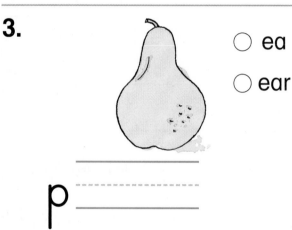

○ ea
○ ear

p_____

4.

○ y
○ ey

s_____mbols

5.

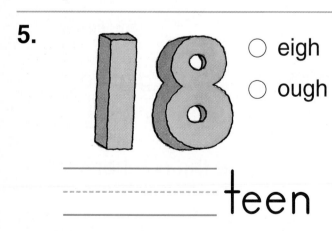

○ eigh
○ ough

_____teen

6.

○ igh
○ ough

d_____

McGraw-Hill School Division

ai
ue
ile

captain	certain	curtain	mountain	fountain
guess	guest	guests		
fertile	missile			

Name_____

Circle the sentence that tells about the picture.

curtain

guest

fertile

I.

~~There were many crops on the fertile land.~~ *(circled)*

The farmer had no crops this year.

2.

There is snow on top of the mountain.

There is fire on top of the mountain.

3.

Take a drink from the water fountain.

Take a drink from the pitcher of water.

4.

Ben is a guest at the party.

Lily is a guest at the party.

5.

The police captain found the lost cat.

The firefighter found the lost cat.

 Helping at Home To help your child practice the *ai, ue,* and *ile* sounds, invite him or her to draw pictures of the following: *captain, mountain, guests, fountain, curtains.* Encourage your child to make up a silly sentence to go with each picture.

Introducing /ə/ *ai*, /e/ *ue*, /əl/ *ile*

A CERTAIN TRIP

by Sharon Gordon
illustrated by Jean Hirashima

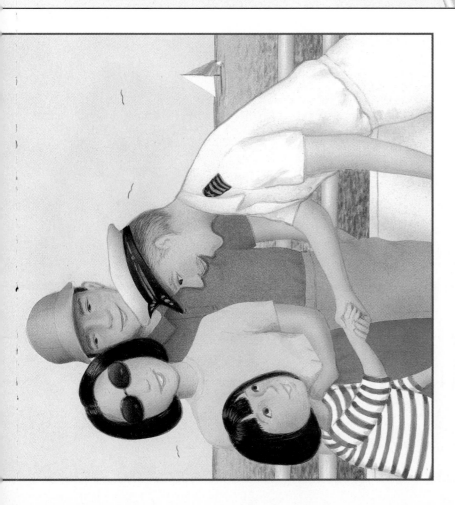

The Captain came to say good night to his guests.

"I knew you'd enjoy your first boat trip," he told Lee.

"I guess you were right," she said.

Then she shook her head.

"No," she said. "I'm **certain** you were right!"

8

Wow! It was amazing. The boat sat in front of Lee like a small mountain. This was her first boat ride. And she was not certain that she would like it. She climbed the steps with the other guests.

"Welcome," said the Captain. "I'm certain you will enjoy the trip."

"I guess so," Lee said softly.

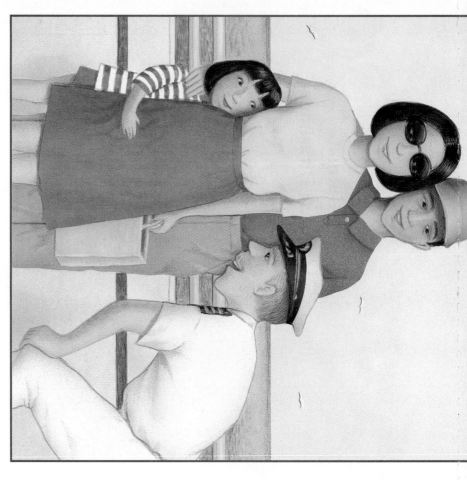

McGraw-Hill School Division

Later, the Captain rang the dinner bell. Lee sat at his large table with her friends. Then they went out to the deck to watch the stars come out.

Suddenly, something that looked like a missile shot across the night sky.

Fireworks! What a great way to end a great day.

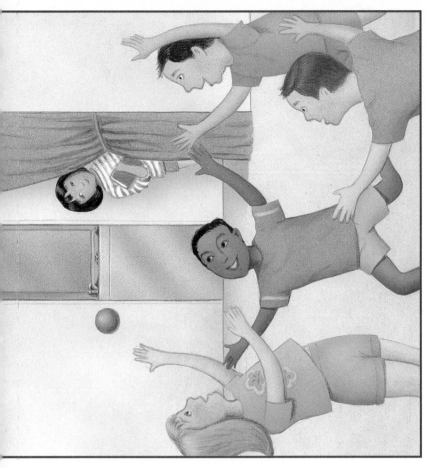

"Anchors away!" cried the Captain. Off they went. Lee watched the boat pull away from the land. Then she peeked around a curtain, shyly.

"I guess I'll just read," she thought. But outside she could see other kids having fun and playing games.

"Do you want to play?" they called. "Join us," they waved.

"I guess so," Lee said.

"Wow, look over there," called a man. There in the middle of the sea was a huge mountain. It was covered with green, fertile grass and wild flowers. Lee was certain she had never seen anything so beautiful.

Lee walked up on deck and looked around. She took a sip from the water fountain. Just then, a ball came crashing down next to her.

"Toss it here," said one boy.

"I guess I could try," she replied. Lee tossed the ball back. Before long, she was having fun with the other kids.

Soon Lee made many new friends. There was so much to do and see.

"Don't you wish we could dive into the water?" someone asked.

"I guess that would be fun," smiled Lee. She thought how it would be to dive in and float in the cool waves. Lee was beginning to be quite certain she liked her first boat trip.

ai
ue
ile

Name_____

Choose the word that completes
the sentence. Write the word.

| certain   curtains   fertile   guess   mountain |

1.

The kitchen curtains are purple.

2.

A snowy _____ is lots of fun!

3.

He is _____ it will rain.

4.

Can you _____ how much I weigh?

5.

The green garden has _____ soil.

Helping at Home Your child is learning to recognize words that have the *ue* sound as in *guest*,
the *ile* sound as in *fertile*, and the *ai* sound as in *certain*. Challenge your child to try to use as many
of the following words as he or she can in a single sentence: *guess, guest, mobile, fountain, mountain*.

Name_____

Circle the word that names each picture.
Write the word.

1. (guest) rest

guest

2. rhythm rough

3. neighbor reindeer

4. obey buy

5. mitten mountain

6. glide guide

7. fountain mountain

8. guy guide

9. building banking

McGraw-Hill School Division

 Helping at Home Play a game of "Twenty Questions" in which you pick out an object in the room. Have your child ask questions that can be answered only with "yes" or "no." Count the number of questions asked. When your child identifies the object, help him or her write its name.

silent
t
n

fasten	often	listen	glisten
castle	whistle	thistle	trestle
hymn	column	solemn	autumn

Name_____

Circle the sentence that tells about the picture.

whistle  autumn

1.

The castle is down in a valley.

⟨The castle is high on a hill.⟩

2.

The chief blows his whistle and cars stop.

The light turns green and cars go.

3.

The train chugged across a trestle bridge.

The train went through a tunnel.

4.
```
  42
  23
+ 11
————
  76
```

The numbers are being subtracted.

The numbers are in a column.

5.

In spring, I listen to the birds.

In autumn, I rake the leaves.

 Helping at Home Play a game of charades. Write the following words on slips of paper: *fasten, listen, whistle, autumn, solemn, column.* Put the slips of paper in a hat and have your child pick one piece of paper. Encourage him or her to act out the word as you guess which word is being portrayed.

AUTUMN RIDE

by Judy Nayer

illustrated by Margaret Sanfilippo

Columns of smoke puffed into the air as the train slowed down. It had reached the station and the end of the autumn ride.

"What a great time!" said Ann and Matt as they got off the train. "We should do this often!"

 Helping at Home Your child has read this book in school. Read it aloud together at home. Then have your child find and write the words in the story that have a silent *n* or *t*.

8

Ann and Matt were excited. They often took car trips in autumn to see the bright leaves. But this time they were taking a train ride. Neither one had ever taken a train before.

"This is not just any train," said Dad. "This is an old steam train."

"Listen!" said Mom. "I think I hear it!"

"Whoo!" The train whistle warned, "Here I come!"

Next the train coasted down the mountain. Soon they were in the valley.

"Clang! Clang!" It was a boat taking people for an autumn ride on the lake. They listened to the clang of the bell as the boat headed for shore.

The train whistled back. "Whoo! Whoo!"

A column of smoke filled the sky.
"I can see the train!" yelled Matt.
At last the train rolled into the station. It was big and shiny. It glistened in the sun. Ann and Matt listened to the brakes screech as the train stopped.
"Let's go!" said Mom and Dad.
Ann and Matt climbed up the train's steps.
"We're on our way!" said Dad.

The train slowed down as it climbed up a mountain. It huffed and puffed all the way to the top.
At the top of the mountain was a castle. Tall stone columns stood beside the doorway. Two men watched with solemn faces.
"Wow!" said Ann and Matt.

The train gave a short blast of its whistle and pulled out of the station. "Puff, chuff. Puff, chuff." Soon they left the city behind.

It was a beautiful day. The autumn leaves glistened in the sun. Ann liked the reds and yellows best.

The train picked up a little speed. Ann and Matt listened to the wheels clack faster and faster.

McGraw-Hill School Division

The train roared past towns and farms. Matt spotted horses grazing. Ann waved to some hikers.

Next the train went past apple trees and over a trestle, a kind of bridge. It gave a warning with its whistle. "Whoo! Whoo! Click–clack. Click–clack." The train sang its song as it zigzagged along.

silent
t
n

Name _____

Choose the word that completes the sentence.
Write the word.

| whistle   glisten   columns   castle   autumn |

1.  The Romans made buildings with  columns .

2.  The _____ leaves are beautiful.

3. 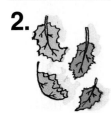 I am learning to _____ .

4.  Snow can _____ in the sun.

5.  This old stone _____ is huge.

 Helping at Home Write these silent *n* and *t* words on cards: *column, whistle, castle, listen, solemn, autumn.* Have your child pick a card and start a poem using the word on the card. Then pick another word and continue the poem. Take turns until all the cards have been picked.

Name _____

Fill in the circle in front of the word that names each picture.

1.
● glisten
○ disguise

2.
○ collar
○ column

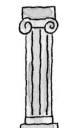

3.
○ comb
○ curtain

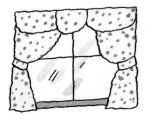

4.
○ cough
○ thought

5.
○ buy
○ guy

6.
○ fasten
○ fountain

7.
○ mystery
○ mountain

8.
○ listen
○ glisten

9.
○ calf
○ cough

 Helping at Home Write these words on paper: *whistle, column, fountain, curtain, building, symbol.* Join your child on a treasure hunt in which he or she tries to find the objects listed. Check off each item when it is found.

McGraw-Hill School Division

Name _____

Circle the missing letters. Then write them.
Read the words.

1.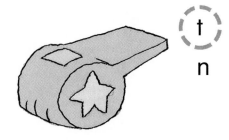
t
n

whis__le

2.
eigh
ough

c _____

3.
eigh
ough

sl _____

4.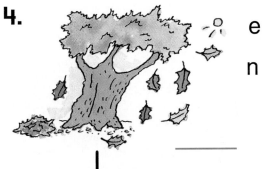
e
n

autum____

5.
ai
ue

mount____n

6.
ui
ai

disg____se

Helping at Home Write the letters *t, n, ai, ue, uy, ui, ough* on small squares of paper.
On another sheet of paper, in large print, write: whis__le, autum__, fount__n, g__st, b__, g__de,
and t__. Help your child insert the correct letters to complete each word.

Name_____

Circle the word that names each picture.
Write the word.

1.  (fasten) listen	**2.**  glisten whistle	**3.** 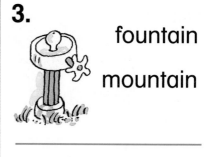 fountain mountain
fasten		
4.  curtain certain	**5.**  neighbor neither	**6.**  guess guest
7.  captain castle	**8.**  disguise distance	**9.** 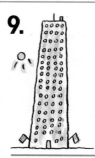 building buying

 Helping at Home Keep a journal with your child. Read journal entries together, listening carefully for sounds in words. If a word is misspelled, play "Three Guesses," listening for the sounds in the words and thinking of the different ways the sound may be spelled.

McGraw-Hill School Division

Word List

ir, ur

bird
birds
birth
burn
burned
burning
chirp
curl
curled
curls
dirt
fir
first
fur
girl
girls
hurled
hurt
nurse
purr
purse
returned
shirt
sir
skirt
stir
surprise
surprised
third
turn
turned
turnip
turtle
turtles

or, ar

actor
afterwards
backward
caterpillar
cellar
collar
color
doctor
doctor's
dollar
dollars
favor
favorite
flavor
forward
harbor
lizard
onward
sailor
tailor
word
words
work
worked
worker
world
worms
worse
worth

ay

always
away
bay
birthday
clay
day
daydream
driveway
Friday
gray
holiday
hurray
lay
May
may
maybe
okay
pay
paying
play
played
playing
plays
ray
rays
relay
Saturday
say
someday
spray
sprayed
stay
stayed
stray
swayed
today
tray
way
yesterday

y

butterfly
by
cry

crying
dry
fly
fry
lying
my
myself
nearby
pry
sky
Sly
sly
Sly's
try
trying
type
why

y

any
anymore
anyone
baby
body
country
cozy
creamy
creepy
crunchy
dairy
diary
dirty

dizzy
easy
every
everybody
everybody's
everyone
fairy
fifty
frisky
funny
furry
handy
happy
Harry
hungry
hurry
Jenny's
Lady
lady
Lady's
lazy
lucky
many
nosy
party
plenty
pony
pretty
rocky
Sandy's
shiny
sleepy

sorry
story
tasty
tiny
tummy
twenty
very
Widdy
Widdy's
worry

ly, ey

carefully
Donkey
donkey
family
finally
happily
hardly
honey
key
luckily
money
monkey
monkeys
only
quickly
quietly
really
sadly
safely
shortly
shyly

silly
slowly
softly
suddenly
sweetly
valley

soft c

celebrate
celebrating
celery
cell
cellar
cent
center
cents
cereal
circle
circles
circus
city
concert
dance
danced
dancers
decide
decided
except
excited
exciting
face
faces
fancy

fence
ice
lacy
medicine
mice
nice
nicely
notice
office
once
paces
pencil
place
race
raced
recipe
recipes
sentence
slice
space
spice
spicy
twice

soft g

age
bandage
cage
change
charge
damage
fringe
general

gentle
gentleman
George
Gerald
germ
giant
gigantic
gingersnap
gingersnaps
giraffe
giraffe's
large
manage
page
stage
stingy
strange
stranger
teenager
teenagers
tragic

dge

badge
bridge
budge
budget
dodge
dodged
edge
edged
fudge
grudge

hedge
judge
ledge
ledges
lodge
Midge
nudge
nudged
pledge
pledged
ridge
smudge
smudged

sion, tion

action
addition
admission
attention
celebration
condition
decision
decoration
definition
description
direction
education
explanation
expression
interruption
invention
invitation
lotion

mansion
motion
nation
occasion
permission
position
question
solution
station
television
vacation
vision

short oo

book
bookstore
brook
cook
cookbook
cookbooks
cooking
cooks
door
doorway
foot
football
good-bye
hood
hook
looked
looking
looks
nook

shook
stood
took
understood
wood
wooden
wool
woolly

long oo
afternoon
balloon
bloom
boom
boomed
boot
boots
broom
choose
chooses
classroom
cool
food
fooled
goof
goofy
goose
hoot
loop
loops
loose
moon
Moon's

moose
noon
oops
pool
poor
proof
roof
room
school
smooth
smoothly
soon
spoon
stool
stools
stoop
swoop
tablespoons
tool
whoops
zoo

ow
below
blow
blowing
blown
bow
bowl
elbow
elbows
fellow
flow

flowed
flown
follow
glow
glowing
grow
growing
grown
grows
hollow
low
marshmallow
marshmallows
mow
mowed
mower
owe
own
pillow
row
rowing
shadow
shadows
showed
slow
slowed
slowly
Snow
snow
Snow's
sparrows
swallow
swallows

throw
thrown
tomorrow
window
yellow

ou
announcer
around
bounce
bounced
bout
cloud
count
counted
country
couple
course
court
double
famous
flour
found
four
fourth
ground
group
hound
hours
house
mound
mount
mouse

mouse's
mouth
our
out
outside
pound
round
round-off
shout
shouted
sound
sounded
sounds
soup
sour
south
touch
trouble
trout
workout
you'll
young
younger
youngster
yours

long u

Bruce
bugle
costume
cube
cure
cute

duke
flute
future
huge
Judy
Judy's
June
Lucy
lute
museum
music
perfume
picture
prune
pure
rude
rule
secure
super
sure
tube
tune
uniform
unite
use
using
usual
utensil

ue, ui

blue
bruise
clue

clues
cruise
cruised
due
fruit
glue
glued
juice
juicy
Sue
suit
suitcase
suits
true
Tuesday

oi, oy

annoy
boil
boy
boys
broil
choice
coin
enjoy
enjoying
foil
join
joint
joy
loyal
moist
moisture

noise
noisy
oil
oyster
point
pointed
pointing
Roy
royal
spoil
toy
voice

ew, eau

beautiful
beauty
blew
chew
chewy
crew
dew
drew
few
flew
grew
news
newspaper
screw
stew
threw

aw, au

awful
because
cause
cautiously
claw
claws
crawl
crawls
dawn
fault
fawn
hauled
haunt
hawk
hawk's
jaw
law
lawn
Paul's
pause
paw
raw
sauce
saucer
sausage
saw
shawl
somersault
straw
yawn

ph, gh

alphabet
autograph
autographs
elephant
elephants
laugh
laughing
laughter
microphone
nephew
orphan
pharmacy
Phillip's
phone
photo
photograph
photos
phrase
telephone

ch

ache
aches
anchor
anchors
character
characters
chemistry
chord
chorus
chrome
echo
mechanic
mechanical
orchestra
school
stomach

ch

Charmaine
chef
Chicago
chute
machine
machinery
parachute

silent w

wrap
wrapper
wreck
wriggle
wring
wrinkle
wrist
wrists
write
writer
writing
wrong
wrote

silent k

knapsack
knead
knee
kneel
knew
knife
knight
knit
knitted
knob
knock
knot
know
knowledge
known
knows
knuckle

silent b

climb
climbed
comb
crumb
doubt
dumb
lamb
limb
numb
plumber
thumb

silent l

calf
calm
chalk
could
couldn't
folks
half
palm
should
sidewalk
stalk
stalked
talking
walk
walked
walking
would

silent g, h, gh

bright
caught
daughter
daylight
exhausted
exhibit
fight
flight
ghostly
gnat
gnaw
gnome
high
honest
honor
hour
light
might
mighty
moonlight
night
nights
oh
right
sigh
sighs
sight
sign
slightest
straight
taught
thigh
tight
tightly
whoops
whoosh

ea

already
bread
break
breakfast
breaks
breath
daybreak
dead
deaf
dread
feather
great
greatest
head
headed
headstand
health
healthy
heavy
instead
lead
leather
meadow
meant
pleasant
read
ready
spread
steady
steak
sweat
thread
wealthy
weather

ear

bear
early
earn
earth
heard
heart
hearth
learn
learning
pear
pearl
search
searching
tear
wear
wearing

ie, ei

achieve
achievement
babies
belief
believe
berries
brief
ceiling
chief
either
field
grief

grieve
ladies
niece
neither
pennies
piece
puppies
receive
received
relief
relieve
shield
shriek
thief
yield

ei, eigh, ey
eight
eighteen
freight
hey
neigh
neighbor
neighbors
neighed
obey
obeyed
prey
reindeer
reins
sleigh

vein
weigh
weight

ough
although
bought
cough
coughed
dough
doughnut
enough
fought
ought
rough
though
thought
through
tough
trough

y, ui
build
building
builds
built
crystal
guild
guilty
gym
gymnast
gymnastics

gymnasts
mystery
myth
physical
physician
physics
rhythm
symbol

uy, ui
buy
buyer
buying
disguise
disguised
disguises
guide
guided
guiding
Guy
Guy's

ai, ue, ile
captain
certain
curtain
fertile
fountain
guess
guessed
guest
guests

missile
mountain

silent t, n
autumn
castle
column
columns
fasten
glisten
glistened
hymn
listen
often
solemn
thistle
trestle
whistle
whistled

High-Frequency Words
about
could
good
look
new
our
talk
walk
where

A B C D

E F G H

I J K L

M N O P

McGraw-Hill School Division

d	c	b	a
h	g	f	e
l	k	j	i
p	o	n	m

McGraw-Hill School Division

Q	R	S
T	U	V
W	X	Y
Z		

McGraw-Hill School Division

s	r	q
v	u	t
y	x	w
		z

McGraw-Hill School Division